My Road

A Runner's Journey Through
Persistent Pain to Healing

Julie B. Hughes

First published by Run to Write 2021

First Edition
Print ISBN: 9781737690719

The information quoted "Bobbi Gibb was an artist. When she looked out from behind her bushes she saw in the stream of runners a stream of consciousness, not a race, not a competition. She slipped into the

Dedication

To my dearest husband, Jeff, you love me even in the messy bits. Thank you for always cheering me on and supporting my running. To my beautiful children, Brindsley and Delaney, thank you for teaching me how to love myself and love you unconditionally. I always wanted a son and daughter just like you. I love you so much.

Contents

Introduction

My dream of running the Boston Marathon hung in the balance.

As a child, I learned about this world-famous event from other runners, coaches, and books. It was a big deal. The most elite runners were there, and if I qualified by running the time standard for my age group then I could be among them! The history, the spectators, the tradition — it's a marathon most runners strive for. I was no different.

Two women runners I read about, Katherine Switzer and Bobbi Gibb, inspired my dream. Even though technically women weren't allowed to run the Boston Marathon in 1967, they boldly did it anyway. As a kid, I thought, *Wow, these women are brave! I want to be like them, a brave marathoner.* They proved to the world that women can race the 26.2-mile distance without having their uteruses fall out! Ridiculous, right? Anyway, I wanted to be among these women who crossed the finish line. I loved to run and felt deep down that the marathon distance was meant for me. My dream would be achieved that year, I vowed, in 2003 — but pain, my great protector was getting in the way.

Now, in 2021, I don't have all the answers, but my pain experience helped me better understand the truth that everything matters. There is no separation between the mind and body. Pain is sensory and emotional. This shifted my thinking beyond my tissues, muscles, and joints to look at myself as a whole person, and to consider my brain to be the best tool of all. In the chapters that follow, you will read some of what I faced to achieve my dream of running the Boston Marathon, complete with poems I wrote to help me get there. I hope my story inspires you to keep running your race, to go after your dreams, and never give up. On your mark, get set, courage!

Chapter One
Choosing to Run

Running
above the ground
moving, flying, breathing
my freedom to leave any time
Let's bolt

I was in first grade when I laced up my first pair of running sneakers, Reebok, which were all white, brand new, and *not* hand-me-downs. I loved the new sneaker smell when I opened the box, and I couldn't wait to run in them. At school, chasing the boys and playing tag were my favorite things to do. I felt like I was flying, like I was free. Most importantly, I didn't have to wear a dress. My mom always wanted me to wear dresses. I would cry and pout about it, but no one wears a dress while running, and I wanted to do more of it.

I could run anytime, anywhere, and I was grateful my parents were too busy with the farm to worry about where I was going. I would run alone down to the cemetery and back, or up to the church and back. I was a tomboy. I loved playing in the dirt making mud pies, looking for toads by the pond, and playing G.I. Joe with my cousin.

My uncle Tim was an avid runner. He got me involved in running clubs and road races, and he brought me along to running events. We got a special yellow T-shirt to wear when we arrived at the road races. I put the shirt on over my ponytail, standing taller as a smile came across my face. I toed the line with all the runners, music playing over a loudspeaker, and the announcer speaking into a microphone. There were cheers as we ran and snacks after the race. It was a big party, and I was invited! It was so much fun, and running at this age was never about winning, pace, or who I could beat. Running made me happy because it was my playtime. But something inside of me changed the more I ran. I wanted to be fast, and I wanted to be good at something. As my cousin and I both enjoyed running more and more, it sparked my competitive spirit.

It was always a joy when my uncle took me to run events and races. Lynn Jennings was a professional runner who I looked up to, and one time my uncle took me to an event where she was speaking. I couldn't wait and was so excited to go. I sat next to my uncle and stared at her while she spoke. Lynn talked about her running career in such a calm and confident way. I loved that her legs were so muscular — just like mine — and she made a comment about her "bigger than other runners' legs" in a proud and easygoing way. That made me feel good about my body. *I look like her,* I thought. I got an autographed poster and hung it on my wall right when I got home. I had a few other running

posters and would look at them every day in my room.
Lynn Jennings was fast and a tough runner. I wanted to be
just like her.

One of the many running posters that hung on my bedroom walls

When it came to running, I always showed up and it
changed my mood from sad or upset to happy and calm.
Running was my escape. It was my way of dealing with
emotional pain. I would lace up my sneakers and head out
the door to the sound of the wind or birds. Then it was just
my breathing and my feet hitting the pavement. There was
no criticism, no judgment. It was just me, alone, and I liked
that. I liked being alone. There was a sense of comfort and
safety for me on the roads.

I found that running was decreasing my worry and fear,
replacing those emotions with a sense of inner calm and

contentment. The longer I ran the better I felt, and so I kept running. Running for an hour was no big deal to me, which was why the marathon distance intrigued me. I wanted to have a reason to be out on the roads longer. I wanted to have this feeling last longer.

***

It's freshman year and I slouch in my chair, my eyelids getting heavier. I attempt to take notes, but my teacher's monotone voice keeps getting quieter and quieter. I feel my hand stop, my eyes close. I just want to sleep, and for a moment I do. I jerk as her voice suddenly booms into my ears. I quickly open my eyes and look around, making sure no one has noticed. I get back to taking notes.

When our farm workers quit, I had to fill in until new people were hired. During that time, 3:30 a.m. chores were expected of me before heading to school. Just about every day, the alarm's *beep, beep, beep* would wake me with a start. For a second, I'd forget why I was waking up and I'd pull the covers up and fall back to sleep. *Oh, crap! I slept in, it's 4 a.m.*

I'd rush downstairs to get my barn clothes on, sliding into jeans with manure stains and a hand-me-down sweatshirt before throwing on my Carhartt jacket, lacing up my boots, and racing out the door.

The cold air hits my face, and suddenly I'm wide awake. My chest tightens, my stomach turns as I run through the field to the barn. I'm scared. I don't like when my dad yells, his hat turned to the side, his face red and his arms flying around in anger. I know being late is a problem and my body senses it.

I don't like feeling this in my body. I start yelling at myself before I even get to the barn: You're so stupid. Why didn't you get up on time? Dad is going to be mad at you. It's your fault if he is. The torment has already started and my body tenses up more. I want to cry. I force myself to hold it in as I slide open the wooden door to enter the barn. The gentle swishing sound of the milking machines relaxes me for a moment. I see my mom. Her smile and good morning wave give me some reassurance that all is well. My dad, carrying a milking machine to the next cow, doesn't say a word. He ignores me. I take this as a sign to get to work, don't talk. He is not happy with me. I don't talk much to my dad. I'm afraid to. My body feels confined and weak, not like when I run. Running is my good buddy, just me, the road, and a pair of sneakers.

I would sometimes bring my black Sony Walkman along on runs if I could find batteries, with my playlist blasting Michael Jackson, The Bangles, and Pat Benatar. I could run for hours, singing along without a care in the world. I allowed myself to be a kid. It was a time I truly felt free and strong without the pressure and responsibility of the dairy farm chores waiting for me. My body would relax, and I focused on breathing, pumping my arms, and putting one foot in front of the other. This is why I loved running so much, and why I met myself out on the road every day.

I want to hug Julie as a little girl so hard for choosing to run in the dark, the rain, the snow, and the sunshine. Choosing to run no matter what. If it wasn't for running, I may not have kept going. I may have stayed in the trenches of self-doubt, self-sabotage, and a victimhood mindset. I may have accepted my pain and given up. Running saved us, little girl. We made it!

Me at one of my many road race parties

Chapter Two
Dairy Farm Kid

Running from shame
Was the way I came
It wouldn't let me go
So I went with the flow
I didn't realize the harm
It began on the farm
But I've learned its name
Now it's tame, you can do the same.

I started paying attention to my inner critic at a young age. She's been bugging me ever since. She likes to tell me I'm fat, ugly, stupid, and not good enough. I believed her, and it was pretty easy too. My parents weren't the kind to get all in your business unless you weren't at the barn when you were supposed to be. Taking me aside to ask, "What's on your mind?" or having a conversation other than the farm chores was rare. They were running a dairy farm. There wasn't time for this kind of interaction.

My parents worked hard. My siblings and I were expected to participate in the family dairy farm operations, no questions asked. Most of my chores were the same day in and day out: milk cows, feed the calves, sweep the barn, and feed hay to the cows. Washing the milking machines in a shiny steel sink full of soapy suds was my favorite. There was something relaxing, meditative, about the warm bubbles covering my hands as I washed the parts of the machine. It was me, alone, making them sparkle.

Cleaning the outside of the milking tank with warm soapy water with a large handle brush was another job to be done. I remember the big steel milking tank sparkling, and my reflection looking back at me.

Cleaning out the calf hutches was a pain in any season. In winter, you're freezing — but at least the poop is frozen. In warmer months, you're sweating and it's a messier job. The calf hutches were so small I would have to hunch over so I wouldn't hit my head on the top. Many times I did, muttering under my breath, "I hate this," as I stopped to rub my head. A calf grabbed my sleeve with its long pink tongue, sucking on my jacket, nudging me with its little head, trying to get my attention. I was annoyed, her slobber now all over me. I just wasn't in the mood to pet her. I kept working instead, using the pitchfork to remove her mess from the bedding then placing new straw down for her.

We had a tie-stall barn for milking the cows. Fresh hay or feed was placed in front of each stall to entice the cow to enter. They were stationary during milking. We had eight milking machines, four used on each side. They weighed at least ten pounds. We would carry the milking machines from each cow until we got to the end of the barn. Before placing the machine on a cow's udder, she needed to be cleaned well and milked by hand a few times to check that her milk looked healthy, not clumped up or bloody. Some of the cows could get mastitis or infection, so we needed to check before milking them.

There were times I got kicked by the cows. Some were just a little more freaked out than others. I was taught to place my hand on them to let them know I was there, not to startle them. I would pat them and speak kindly, saying something like, "It's okay, it's okay, we are going to milk you." I needed to stay calm. That usually helped the cow stay calm. It didn't always work. Some would move, kick, or turn their head at me, mooing loudly. I didn't have time to be afraid. They needed to be milked, so I just worked on those cows as quickly as I could, praying I wouldn't get kicked. I got to know the cows very well. I knew which ones were cranky and which ones were not.

If a cow sneezes while going to the bathroom, watch out — that shit will fly! Consider yourself lucky if it hits your back and not your face. There were plenty of times I got splattered, thank goodness always on my clothes. I felt a lot of pressure with all the responsibilities of the farm. I kept a list in my head of what I had to do next. I didn't want to forget anything or let my dad down. I didn't want him to get angry.

Our farm was very well kept compared to our home. My dad took pride in that. He was very particular on how he wanted the job done, though he never said in words what he expected. We watched him, praying we did the job right the first time. My dad didn't have time to stop and teach. He was rushing to the next thing, dealing with a piece of broken machinery, or driving around to find a part. I wondered, *Does he think we can read his mind?* I did my best to figure out what he wanted, but for me it was nerve-racking. The chance of doing something wrong meant getting screamed at, then the silent treatment for a week or more.

My mom would manage the house, the farm, and five children. The sink was full of dishes, the unswept floor was covered with pieces of hay or straw as you entered the house, and laundry was piled high on the dryer. I took it upon myself to fill and empty the dishwasher, do the laundry, and sweep. I was embarrassed by our home. It was dirty most of the time. I took pride in cleaning it up just in case someone stopped over. We rarely had company, but occasionally my grandparents or friends would stop in. When they did, I wanted the kitchen to look nice. It was the first thing you saw when you came into our worn-out home. The upstairs, where my bedroom was, was so cold in the winter that I wore a hat and mittens to bed to keep warm. I didn't like the winter months. I felt like I couldn't get warm. Working outside on the farm in the snow was difficult. My fingers and toes would freeze, and I could hardly move them. I couldn't wait to get my chores done to go home and warm up. Most winters were like this, bundling up, doing chores, and being grateful for hand-me-down sweaters, coats, and scarfs. This was the plan I had to stick to as a child. It was building perseverance, fortitude, grit. It was also why running outside in all weather wasn't a big deal.

***

I wanted to help my mom. She looked tired sitting at the kitchen table with her tea and buttered toast, staring at the checkbook. There was constant financial stress. Fights between mom and dad broke out often, mostly about the farm and money.

The yells startle me, my body tenses up. My stomach is in knots. I want to get away. I don't want to feel this in my body, so I grab my running sneakers and head out the door. I breathe in the fresh air, look at the road, thankful that I don't have to listen to the yelling, thankful that I can run.

I still don't know how my parents managed to provide as much as they did for us. I know they had some help, which I am grateful they were willing to accept. Now that I'm a mother, I can see why the house chores were not first on the list; who cares about the dishes or the floor when there are five children to take care of, their activities, and the farm to help manage? I can't imagine the stress and worry they were experiencing. I'm sure it was difficult.

We were fortunate enough to have the staples in our home of bread, eggs, and milk. My grandpa had a chicken farm about eight miles from our home. He would sell his eggs to a local bakery shop. He often dropped off day-old bread for us to eat. We would examine it carefully before spreading the peanut butter and jelly over a slice. On occasion, some loaves had white cottony fuzz growing or black spots. We were told to "pick that off" or "don't eat that slice."

At 4 a.m. I would make myself a PB&J sandwich before getting on my barn clothes. I wasn't hungry, but it helped me wake up. I dragged some mornings. You could say it was my caffeine to get going. It was my way of comforting myself as I walked over to the barn. I was thankful for the dark, calm morning as I trudged through the field preparing myself for what was ahead. My thoughts shifted to the taste of the peanut butter, my mind occupied with chewing, not the farm chores or what kind of mood I would be confronted with.

It was during this time I met Fear. Fear was not fun to be around. He was very bossy and demanding. The more I was around him, the more on edge I became. I would tense up, my stomach would ache, my heart would race. The alarm was constantly going off, but Fear was not going anywhere. He was very unpredictable, making me wonder if I should run or stay. My chest would tighten, I couldn't speak. Fear was in charge. I decided I would do all I could to prevent Fear from showing up. That was a very high standard to set for myself, but that was my new narrative. Is this what triggered the people-pleasing and perfectionist behavior? I'm not certain. What I was certain of was the story I was telling myself: *Don't do anything wrong, don't mess up, do what you are told, and then you will be loved.*

The farm work, running, and school kept me busy. I would fall asleep very quickly at night. I was exhausted. I slept soundly most nights, except if the cows got out. My dad would yell from the bottom of the stairs, "COWS ARE OUT, GET UP, LET'S GO!" His yell would give me a jolt, waking me abruptly from a lovely dream. My adrenaline would rush through my body as I quickly jumped out of bed. I didn't like this feeling, the knots in my stomach, the tension in my body, my heart racing, and my chest tightening. I didn't know what to do about it, so I would pray. I prayed a lot. *Please God let us get the cows back in quickly, please keep my dad calm, and keep us safe.*

When the cows got out in the middle of the night, I wanted to die. I hated when this happened. I was mad at the brave cow who decided to jump the fence. Cows aren't the smartest animals. Chasing them around the uneven fields in the dark with a stick to herd them was not smart either, in my opinion. I could hardly see. The tractor lights were turned on to give us some light, but it was difficult. I wanted to go back to my bed and hide under the covers. I didn't want to help with this job. I did not choose this.

***

I was sitting in the truck, the smell of manure filling my nostrils as I looked down at my boots, my mom sitting motionless in the driver's seat. A Beatles song was on the radio. My mom started singing, every word untroubled.

And anytime you feel the pain, hey Jude, refrain,

Don't carry the world upon your shoulders.

How is she so easygoing? I wondered. My dad just blew up at her and she didn't say a word like nothing happened. *Is it the music? The singing?* I was sitting there tense and worried, but she was tapping the steering wheel as she sang her heart out. I found myself humming quietly with her, beginning to feel some ease in my body as we waited. Her singing calmed me, filled me with joy. We would sing in the car, the house, at church, and the barn. When I think back on this memory, maybe singing for my mom was like what running was for me, our escape, a way to let the worry go, to feel free.

No matter how much my dad flipped out, stormed around the house or farm, she remained this anchor of peace. This amazed me. I wanted to be like her. I decided that I would try not to cry or get upset around my dad. I would show him how strong I was. I would not let his words bother me.

I'll pretend that I am fine, I thought. I believed this would make things easier to handle. My mom rarely showed any negative emotion, she was happy and calm humming to herself or singing with the radio on. I never saw her cry. If I did, I don't remember. I knew she wouldn't yell if I wanted or needed something. I felt safe talking to her. The problem was when she said, "Go ask your father." My dad was a roller coaster of emotions. I was walking on eggshells each time I opened the sliding wooden door to the barn. The placement of his hat, his posture around the cows, and the redness of his face. This was not the time to ask him anything. I couldn't find the courage to face him or speak up. I worked in silence.

I would hear kids talk about parties, places they went over the weekend. Fun stuff. My weekend was at the barn milking cows, shoveling shit, or dodging insults. I wanted to play with my friends, but that meant I wouldn't be around to work. There was a school dance, and my friends asked if I was going. I shrugged my shoulders, unable to commit. I wanted to go. I wanted to belong. At the barn, I told my mom about it, and she said, "Go ask your father." *Ugh.* My head lowered as I rolled my eyes. The dreaded, "Go ask your father." *More like, go beg your father.* I hated when she would say that. *Doesn't she know I'm afraid of him?* His demeanor wasn't warm and fuzzy, especially at the barn. I didn't want to plead, though I really wanted to go to the dance. I would be able to leave the barn early, but then a pang of guilt consumed me. *Oh, just stay and work, you don't have to go to the dance.* But then: *Julie, you want to go, you can do this, just ask.* I took a deep breath, my mind battling over what to do.

I built up the courage, lumbered over to my dad to make my request. He said yes, though his harsh face made me feel bad about leaving the chores for someone else. It was like this a lot. I would turn down parties and hangouts with friends because of the guilt, shame, and need to please. Even though that need to please often meant more yelling, insults, or work. I just wanted to be loved and to be seen.

I open the bathroom cabinet and grab the jar. The jar is clear, with no label on it, white paste-like powder sits inside. My mom tells me to use it to help with the pain. I dip my finger in and lather it on the mouth sore at the base of my gums. I use it to cover the sores in my mouth. *These are the worst. I hate using this stuff.* It stings awful but it helps numb the pain so I can eat and drink. This is my routine every month yet deep down I wonder why this happens. *I didn't bite my cheek or tongue, I always know when I do that, it hurts. Why do I keep getting these sores?* As a child, I didn't get an answer. Or was it me thinking I can handle it, so I avoid asking. I don't want to be a bother or a burden to my parents. I don't complain.

***

My uncle would take us hiking and camping in the Adirondacks. I loved climbing those mountains. It was so peaceful, the towering trees with the sunlight peeking through, our boots landing on the dirt trail without much of a sound. Uncle Tim stopped to show us a special plant or naming the kind of trees we passed. The hike was a challenge, but I didn't complain. When I got to the top, my eyes widened at the view. *Wow, What a beautiful sight.* I was so happy to be there, doing something different and seeing, smelling something else other than cows, milking machines, and shit. I know it might sound mean, but I wanted to explore, learn, and play; I didn't want to be working on the farm every day. I was getting tired of it. I secretly wanted to live with my cousins. I wanted what they had. A calm, encouraging, and happy dad. Yet it was on the dairy farm that I learned the meaning of hard work, patience, discipline, and endurance. These were the exact things to become a marathoner runner, the seeds of resilience that I would need to overcome my pain challenge.

The dairy farm helped develop my readiness for training and racing my first marathon.

Readiness one: Pop a Squat

There was no bathroom on the farm, so we would either go in the milk house — at least there was a door — or hide behind the barn or tractor outside. The milk house had a concrete floor with a huge stainless steel milk tank in the middle where all the milk was held. It was the perfect place to squat behind because no one could see me even if they came in. There was no time to head home, there was work to be done. So, this talent was a necessity. This ability to pop a squat is also needed when you're running on the country roads. Duck behind a tree or a bush, do a shimming shake, then off you go. Trust me, when your bladder is full, running is the last thing you want to do.

Readiness two: Hilly Pastures

In the spring, we would head up the hilly pastures in search of baby calves that were born. We prayed it was a boy, not a girl. If the baby was a female, we would keep it and raise it to be milked, which meant no money. If it was a bull, the incentive was money. We would get some of it, which meant I would be able to buy a toy! We rarely got anything new, so this was exciting. I got on my manure boots and poop-stained Carhartt jacket and trudged up the hill to help find this baby calf, praying it was a bull. This was just one of many hikes up those hilly pastures. I would feel a burning sensation in my leg muscles, achiness in my hips as I pushed myself up the hills. These aren't exactly memories I cherish; however, those early hills were giving me strong running legs and building mental toughness, which were exactly two things I needed to finish a marathon.

Readiness three: Hay Bales

In the summer, unloading hay wagons and stacking the hay in the barn was exhausting work. This job, however, not only strengthened my arm, back, and leg muscles, but also developed stamina. I learned to keep working even when I wanted to stop. *We can't stop, keep going, another wagon to unload is waiting.* There was no time for rest, we had to beat the rain or the heat, everything was an urgent matter. This developed my mental strength and perseverance, a must-have when training and racing for a marathon.

Readiness four: Rising Early

Getting up early was a habit I developed as a child. I'm very grateful for it. To some, getting up at 4:00 a.m. or 4:30 a.m. may seem crazy, but for a farm girl, I didn't think twice. It was the norm, and it's what helped me get my marathon training in before my jobs started for the day. This disciplined approach was ingrained in me. I would later discover this was part of my self-care, and I could build from it. Getting up early would be my time to manage my mind.

Readiness five: Farmers Carry

Now I know why they call it "the farmers carry." I've been doing this strengthening exercise since first grade and didn't even know it. The calves were outside in their hutches waiting to be fed. I would carry two large buckets filled with warm milk, one handle of the bucket in each hand, slowly walking out to feed them, being careful not to spill the warm milk on my pants. When I did it would freeze to the pants, which I hated. Frozen milk pants are uncomfortable and smelly! This slow, deliberate carrying of the milk pails was strengthening my spine, leg, and arm muscles. I was mindfully walking, though my thoughts were nothing to repeat to a friend.

On the farm, I picked huge rocks out of the fields and waddled to the wagon to throw them in, with dirt and sweat covering my face and clothes. This was a spring job that I dreaded. Who wanted to pick rocks out of a field? Not me, yet it needed to be done before planting season. It was always the hottest day, or maybe it just felt that way because of the intense energy and work I was putting into it. I forked stinky manure out of the calves' hutches, so they had a nice bed of straw to lie on, and stacked hay bales that sometimes were too heavy to lift. I had to barrel roll them, squatting low and pushing with all my might. It was tough. I could feel the soreness in my back, legs, and arms, but it wasn't permanent.

Maybe I took pride in the pain, that I could handle it. I would be noticed for doing all the work, not complaining. *See me, look at me, Dad. Look at all I'm doing as a way for your approval, your love.*

Chapter Three
The Battle in My Mind

Listen to your body
It knows what to do
Your stomach may feel funny
Your back may tense up too
It's giving you a warning
That something isn't right
Listen to your body
It is your guiding light

When I joined the junior high cross-country and track teams, I was determined to be the best. I could sense that sports were important to my dad, so I wanted to be great at them. I wanted to make him happy. I thought his happiness was my responsibility. I lost the real joy of running in this pursuit. It was now overcome by thoughts of *I need to be faster, thinner, stronger*, and *I need to win*. In my mind if I could achieve those things I would matter. I would be seen. I would be loved. Fear would not show up. This is what I wanted most as a child.

I worked extremely hard in practice, pushing myself at every workout to be the front-runner or in the lead pack. I had no problem performing in practice. I was relaxed and carefree, enjoying the runs through the trails, roads, or on the track. Race days were different. My stomach would turn and knot up, my heart would race, and I could feel this panic inside of me. I was so nervous and worried. *Don't come in last, you have to win, everyone is counting on you.* I was running so well in practice, yet when it came to races, my ability didn't always match up. I would hit times in practice that I wasn't consistent with on race day. It frustrated me and my coaches. The plan going into the race was to get out to the front of the pack, sticking to the lead runners. Sometimes I could deliver and run as expected of me, yet in other races, I could not. I would beat myself up when I ran slower or didn't beat the opposing runner I was supposed to. I didn't ask myself helpful questions like, *What can I learn from this race? What can I do differently?* Instead, I asked, *Why am I not as fast as her, or as thin as her? What is wrong with me?*

Track meets were similar. My practice speed and effort weren't the same or consistent with race days. My worst fear was to come in last place. Everyone was watching each lap. There was this added pressure of performance as each event had a certain number of runners. It wasn't like cross country where hundreds of us would toe the line, starting together. Track was different, with sometimes five girls on the line, sometimes 15. I never wanted to be last. My events were the 1,500 meters, 3,000 meters, and sometimes on a relay team.

We all lined up at the start, a huge group of us. We were running 3,000 meters, or seven-and-a-half laps. I was nervous. We all toed the line. The gun went off. We took off pretty hard, harder than I was prepared for. Just as I was stepping into the inner lane, a girl behind me hit the back of my shoe. I lost my balance, falling face-first on the track. I picked my head up as everyone kept going, and the sting of pain in my knees and the palms of my hands immediately took over. I wanted to lie there, not get up. Instead, I got up, now behind the pack of runners. I felt defeated before I even finished the first lap.

Lap after lap I trailed farther behind. I just couldn't catch up. I realized that I was last as I was getting lapped by the front-runners. I wanted to stop. It was so embarrassing to be lapped. I felt awful as I crossed the finish line in last place. I cried after the race under the bleachers and hid from my team. I didn't know how to handle this loss or what to do with all these emotions. I couldn't understand why I wasn't running like I was in practice. I was working hard and doing all the training runs that were asked of me. *Why is my performance on race day different?* I didn't know my mind was the piece that was affecting my performance on race day. My training was solid, but my mind was negative and critical.

High school running buddies

It was cross-country season, my favorite. I loved running through the woods, challenging myself up the hills, and the massive start line of all the schools in their colored jerseys elbow to elbow. It was a Saturday invitational. There were at least 20 schools there. The course, through the woods, was fairly hilly. As I previewed the course, I loved it! There were great corners for the opportunity to surge, there were some steep hills with the downhill to catch any front-runners, and a grassy opening to the finish. I got out front with the lead pack of runners right as the gun went off. It narrowed as you got into the woods, and the coach wanted me to get in a good position. I did exactly as we planned and got out with the lead pack of girls. We stayed together for the first mile, then I pulled ahead. I climbed the hill, then cruised down the other end. I was first! I was now running scared. *Don't look back, just keep on pushing, surge around every corner.* I didn't want to be caught. I never looked back.

High school cross country; Running in the woods was my favorite

I flew down the hills, raced around the turns in the woods to gain more of a lead. As I saw the finishing shute up ahead, I heard my coach shout, "GO, kick it in!" I pushed hard to the finish making sure I crossed the line first. I won! I was so happy and proud of myself, a huge smile across my face as I was bent over catching my breath. The smile quickly faded as my dad's words, "You could've run faster." That sentence pierced my ears, and my heart, which had been full of joy, burst. I was hurt, confused, and sad. I ran as fast as I could. I won. Didn't that matter?

This stuck with me all through my high school running career. The battle in my mind grew. The thoughts of *You have to win, you have to run faster and be the best* consumed me, and the joy of running was lost. I almost dreaded the races. I was so worried I wouldn't do well, or I wouldn't run to everyone's expectations. It was something I couldn't live up to, and the pressure weighed on me.

I would be criticized for not running fast enough. I would hear my chest was too big for a runner, my thighs and calf muscles too bulky. I didn't know how to take these comments. I became very confused about my body, and self-critical. I would wear sports bras all day at school to hide my chest. I would often opt out of eating at lunchtime. I was a kid who got free lunch, and I would get picked on for it. It was just easier for me not to wait in line with my tray of food announcing free lunch to the cashier. The room seemed to conveniently go quiet, just at that moment. The stares burned into me. The cashier would grab her sheet of paper to confirm this to be true as I held up the line, wanting to disappear. I would feel a warmth cover my body, my face flush, and my chest tighten. *That feeling again, that feeling I've already felt so many times at home, it's now at school.* I didn't like that feeling. I would avoid the school lunch line because of it. Instead of eating I would play in the gym, usually basketball, or sit at the lunch tables to work or talk with friends as they ate. This became a habit that was not helpful for my mind or body, yet it was something I could control.

***

My uncle organized the Bloom Run. It took place every year around my grandparents' wedding anniversary. We would run a two-mile loop on the roads by my grandparents' home. The winner's name would be etched in a wooden plaque with a silver spray-painted sneaker on it. It's funny because the sneaker is not one you would wear running, it's a high-top basketball-looking sneaker, but my goal was to get my name on it. I thought it was super cool. I wanted to win. Over the years, my uncle won many times, but in 1991 my cousin won. I was bummed because I was on the cross-country and track teams, and in comparison, I was running a lot more. I thought I was fast enough to win, not yet. I began to feel this pressure to win every year the event took place. I would hear, "Julie is fast," and, "She will win, she's been running a lot more than everyone else and she's on the cross-country team." Yet I didn't win, and my negative self-talk was consuming me. *Why can't I run faster? I wish I could keep up with my cousin.*

I was entering 10th grade. I was running a lot over the summer to get ready, my competitive spirit kicking in. *I'm going to win this year,* I told myself confidently as I arrived at my grandparent's house for the annual Bloom Run. My mom drove up the gravel driveway with all us kids, parking by the chicken farm, in line with the other cars. When the race started, my cousin was out in front. I was behind him with my oldest sister. There was about one mile left when I decided, *I'm going to catch him.* I don't remember if I said anything to my sister, I just remember taking off. Keeping my eyes focused on my cousin, watching his feet, and trying to match his speed. I started talking to myself, *I'm going to catch him. I can catch him. I can do this. I want to win.*

I kept my eyes glued on my cousin's back as I picked up my pace and pumped my arms. My determination grew as I kept repeating, *I will catch him, I can do this.* As I got closer and closer, my confidence increased. I got right up next to him with the finish line in sight. We were stride for stride, breathing hard as we could, watching our grandparent's house get closer. I was not going to let up. I saw the finish, my grandma sitting in a chair with the timer in her hand. I started to push harder and pulled ahead. I was first! I sprinted with all I had left, crossing the finish line. I won the Bloom Run! I finally won! My name would be etched in the wooden trophy, with the date 1996.

The Bloom Run Trophy

I was so happy and proud of myself! I did what I set out to do. I've been running this every year since 1988 intending to win, I finally achieved it. I wanted to celebrate, I wanted to smile and be happy for myself, but my thoughts stopped me. The good feelings quickly drained from my body, the voice getting louder in my head, *Don't brag Julie, don't be so happy, and don't show off.* My brain wouldn't allow the feelings of joy, pride, and accomplishment but instead offered the thoughts, *I'm not good enough, what is wrong with me,* and *I've got to work harder.* These were easily accessible thoughts because they were so heavily ingrained, like a paved road in my mind.

I quickly composed myself, said, "Good job!" to my cousin, and shrugged off the win like it was no big deal. I was so hard on myself. I had no idea how harmful that was. The negative self-talk was affecting my mental and physical health though I wasn't making the connection. I didn't know how to be kind to myself. These thoughts — *I am a strong runner, I am good enough,* and *I will achieve my goals* — were fleeting.

I would look around at my teammates thinking, *I wish I was as good as her, as thin as her.* I didn't like how I looked. I became focused on my body, believing I needed to lose weight to run faster. The messages in my head were not true, helpful, or kind. It was easy to believe them though because the words I would hear from people close to me were very similar. I believed every single one and they became my truth: *I am not worthy, I am not lovable, I do not matter.* The one thought that was the loudest, *What is wrong with me?* played over and over. I had no idea that these thoughts mattered. I would soon learn that these thoughts were a contributor to my pain experience.

Chapter Four
Marathon-Ready

I love to run, it is fun
Especially in the sun
Want to come?
Lace-up your shoes
You have nothing to lose
Leave your worries at the door
You won't need them anymore.

I ran on the country roads, passing by other farms, apple orchards, and barking dogs, my ponytail swaying with every step. I turned onto a dirt road, the sky bright blue and the wind at my back, my mind at ease when I was caught off guard by a ferocious barking. An enormous dog was running my way, a vicious black rottweiler with brown markings. My stomach in knots, my hands sweaty, my heart racing, *What do I do, what do I do?* I began to panic. *Do I keep running? Do I stop? Why is this dog not on a leash!* I slowed down almost to a stop, hoping that would deter him from attacking me, but no luck. He lunged at me, grabbing my left arm in its teeth. I started shrieking, and the dog hung on until the owner grabbed him and pulled him off me. I held back the tears, shaking. I was about two miles from home.

I could hardly walk, let alone run, as my arm throbbed with blood, bite marks becoming visible. A guy pulled up next to me in his truck and said, "Get in, I will take you home. That dog is trouble." He looked kind enough, so I got in his truck, my fear completely shaken out of me. There wasn't enough left to worry if this guy was a creep. The man complained the entire ride to my house about that dog. "It's always running off-leash, barking, and chasing anything it sees." *I will make sure not to go down that road again.* He dropped me off and my mom took me to the family doctor. Luckily, the dog did have proper shots, so I didn't have to worry about rabies.

After that, I ran with rocks in my hands or would pick up a stick if I heard a dog barking. I was a lot more vigilant, picked my route more carefully, and I didn't run with music. I started paying more attention to what surrounded me, the sights, smells, and sounds. I was finding this made running even more desirable. What would I see today on my run? What would I hear or smell?

Sometimes it was the smell of lilacs and listening to the birds, sometimes the sound of children laughing and splashing in their pools (oh, how I wish we had a pool). I would look at the fluffy clouds and imagine different animals in the sky, or hum songs in my head as I watched the cars speed by me, some honking in encouragement.

I recall running one morning down a dirt road, humming to myself. As I looked to the left a man was outside looking in the trunk of his car. The interesting part was this man was buck naked in his slippers, casually grabbing what he needed from his trunk. I quickly looked down and sprinted past him, hoping he didn't see me. I was in shock at that sight. Not that a naked human body is anything to be surprised at, but as a young girl running alone, I was shocked! I never would have expected that on a morning run, but I was learning that anything was possible out on the roads. What would I see? What would I find? It was keeping me going.

Some runs I would find a penny, some a quarter. It was fun to stop, pick the money up, and give it a home.

***

I could see and feel my mom's hesitation when at 18 I told her I wanted to run a marathon. It started with a simple letter in the mail addressed to me.

I remember it like yesterday. The plain white envelope with the purple branding of TNT, a Team in Training at the top left corner. I tore it open, excited to find out what this was.

It was a letter asking me to join their team in training. I would fundraise for the Leukemia and Lymphoma Society

(LLS) while training for a marathon, destination Walt Disney World!

After I read it, I looked at my mom and asked, "Will you go with me to the informational meeting?" I had already made up my mind, I was going to be on that team and run a marathon. The reason was easy, I would do this for Nancy.

Nancy was a running teammate of mine in junior high school who passed away from leukemia in 1995. I was only a year older than her, and it was hard to process. She was so kind, happy, and beautiful. I thought, *Maybe she would have wanted to run a marathon, too.* This would be a way to raise money and run in her memory.

Team in training also linked me up with a local boy, Greyson, who was diagnosed with leukemia. I would fundraise and run in honor of him. Being part of this team gave me a sense of purpose and importance. It gave me something to focus on outside of myself, a reason to keep going.

I wondered why my teammate got leukemia. I asked this question to God. I'm miserable, I don't even want to be here anymore. Why didn't you choose me instead?

That's why the letter came to join the Team in Training. God knew I would need running to keep going. It would be a way to make sense of the loss, take my focus off the pain and give me a purpose. I'll admit I was also selfishly thinking that by running this marathon, I would finally be loved and seen.

The long runs were organized on Sundays. We would all meet at a different location each Sunday to run together. I enjoyed running these longer distances with other runners. It was nice to have the support to get through the mileage. I ran with Jane, who had two young boys. She told me she got into running so she could keep up with her boys and stay healthy. I liked running with her and was glad I could keep up. I met another runner who wanted to run a marathon in every state. When anyone asked me why I ran, I told them about my teammate Nancy.

One Sunday, I couldn't meet up with the team in training. The run would be done on my own. After my barn chores were finished, I planned out a route around my home to cover the distance. It was beginning to snow, so I grabbed my hat and gloves before I headed out the door. The cold air hit my face; my breath was visible as I began my long run uphill. Five miles into the run the roads were covered in a white blanket of snow. Snowflakes were hitting my face, sticking to my eyelashes. It was quiet on the country roads as the snow continued to fall. My body relaxed. My breath was calm and even as I continued to pace myself for the next seven miles.

As I headed down toward the town park, a car pulled up alongside me. It was my mom and dad! I was so surprised. *What are they doing here?* I was shocked! In all the years I had run alone on these roads not once had they been interested in where I was or how I was doing. This wasn't like them. *Is something wrong? Do they need me to come home to do barn chores? No.* They were checking in on me to see how I was doing. I was so happy to see them. They drove by me, and I continued to run. It was so nice to know they cared about me. They didn't need me to stop or help with anything. I could keep running. They were there as supportive parents. They continued to drive alongside me for a few more minutes then headed back home. I felt seen and loved for the first time. I felt a surge of energy as my parents drove away. Their car tracks, visible in the snow, reminded me that they were here, that it wasn't a dream. *I can't believe they came to see how I was doing. Wow!* I mattered, even if it was only for today. I wiped the snow from my eyes, picking up my pace. *I can do this, five more miles.* I shook out my arms as I thought of Nancy. How cool would it be if she was here running with me? Her smile was vivid in my mind as I continued my run. *She is here running with me. Her memory will always be with me. It will get me to the finish.*

My fundraising efforts were going well, but I was still behind my goal. I was getting worried I wouldn't make it, but in the last month of my fundraising I had an outpouring of donations come in and I was overwhelmed with gratitude. I couldn't believe how many people from my community supported LLS. It was a great feeling, and I was excited to run a marathon knowing I had achieved my fundraising goal.

It was awesome to go to Florida in January. Not only was I going to run my first marathon, but I was also going to enjoy Walt Disney World and get a break from the winter weather. My parents were able to come, along with my two younger sisters and my friend from school to cheer me on. My grandparents lived in Florida, and they were going to see me at the finish. I was happy that my parents were both going to get a break from the farm chores.

The night before the marathon, I placed out my purple team in a training singlet, shorts, socks, hat, hydration, and bib number. I didn't want to forget anything. This was one thing Jane shared with me during our long runs. She mentioned she puts everything out the night before to avoid rushing in the early morning or forgetting something. I loved that idea and so I did the same. I didn't want to rush or forget anything. I set my alarm for 4 a.m., excitement and anticipation building inside of me as I tried to close my eyes. *I'm going to run a marathon tomorrow!*

I got on the shuttle to the start line with my team, the excitement in our voices growing louder as we entered the parking lot to the start line. As I stepped off the shuttle, I looked up at the stars overhead and thought about Nancy. *When I get tired or start to feel the pain, I will think of her and not give up,* I decided. I had two bracelets on my wrist, one

in honor of Greyson and one in memory of Nancy. This
would keep me going.

I couldn't believe I was here. I was going to run 26.2 miles,
the longest distance I have ever run. We all huddled
together by the start line under the stars. I made sure to get
next to Jane, I enjoyed running with her during the training
runs and wanted to stay with her. She was so positive and
fun to run with, and very encouraging. The gun went off
and we all started shuffling along, our pace almost a walk,
as we all got going. As we broke free from the crowd little
by little, I made sure to stick with Jane the best I could.
There were so many people, I was surprised to easily find
my family on the side cheering me, my mom holding up
the camcorder to record me as I ran by in the darkness.

I had been running for two hours, and now it was daylight.
I felt like I had just started running again as the sun beat
down on us. I was feeling great and having fun running
alongside Jane, encouraging each other, and hearing the
cheers from the crowd. At about mile 18, Jane pulled ahead
of me. I tried my best to go with her, but I was struggling. I
was starting to hurt, and so I looked at my wrist to remind
myself to keep going, to stay strong. *I can do this.* I grabbed
some hydration from the volunteers and kept going. The
last two miles were amazing. So many people were
cheering, we were running through Walt Disney World,
and the finish was almost in sight. I picked up the pace and
looked ahead. I was almost there. I crossed the finish line

and quickly was wrapped up in a foil blanket to maintain my body temperature. My legs felt like jello, my mind a blur at what I just accomplished. My family hugged me and congratulated me. I was exhausted but overwhelmed with a feeling of joy and pride. *I just ran 26.2 miles,* I thought to myself, *and I want to do it again!*

After finishing the Walt Disney World Marathon, I wanted to run another one. The Boston Marathon immediately came to mind. I told myself that I would qualify and race in Boston. That would be my next goal.

Chapter Five
The Fall

Why wasn't it me, I plea
There is more to life you see
You have what it takes
I know your heartaches
I'm with you and will set you free

I left for college that year to run collegiately. The pressure to do well weighed on me and I needed to be perfect. I found myself comparing my looks and running abilities to my teammates. I did not look like a runner, I told myself. I needed to be thinner and stronger. I was convinced that if I looked more like my teammates I would be as good as them. I wanted to be in the lead pack just like I was in high school.

While most of my teammates were hanging out, partying, and having fun, I was running and trying my hardest to lose weight. My belief continued that if I could get to 100 pounds, then I would run faster and be happy. I would be seen. I would matter. I would be good enough.

I began to restrict my eating, to get up before classes to run, and to hide my inner struggle. I was doing everything perfectly, attending classes, meeting up with the team for runs, and going to my tutoring sessions. I was pretending that everything was fine. I was not fine. I had the constant belief that something was wrong with me, and if I lost weight and ran faster, then everything would be fine. I would feel better, and this inner pain I was carrying would go away.

I was running and lifting weights more, and I was so hungry. The restriction of food then turned into binging and purging. It was a vicious cycle that I had no control over. I knew this was not healthy, but I couldn't stop. I found myself eating alone in my room or car, sometimes in the dark. My food of choice to numb the pain became cookies, M&Ms, or Little Debbie's Swiss Rolls. I would force myself to eat every last one until my stomach hurt, until that pain I could feel instead. I would then panic afterward. *I'm going to get fat.* So the purging began.

I felt so disgusting, and more shame and guilt piled on. I would walk or run afterward, promising myself that I would stop and that I would get help. I didn't do either. My pain persisted. This went on for years, and my dream of running in Boston took a backseat. My energy and focus fixated on food, examining labels to make sure I got the lowest calorie choices, as well as fat. Non-fat or low fat was always my go-to option. I decided to not eat meat anymore, thinking that would help me lose more weight. I went from drinking raw full-fat milk at home to skim milk at college. I would go all day without eating. At night, when hunger pains wouldn't allow me to sleep, I would give in to food. I would overeat, making myself sick.

I lost all my ability to listen to my body when it was hungry and when it was full. Eating food was not about fueling my body to run well, to be healthy; it was how I was coping with my emotional pain. It was my way of hiding and the one thing I could control. The result was an unhealthy relationship with food and myself.

***

It's the summer, I'm back from college and working every day on the farm. I don't want to work on the farm anymore. Why do I keep coming back? It's comfortable, it's what I know. I'm mad at myself for not leaving, for not staying at college, but this guilt consumes me. I think I have to be here to help my mom. To please my dad. Maybe it will be different this time, maybe things will be better. They aren't. I feel trapped, suffocated by the demands and routine expected of me.

Every day is turning into the same: get up at 5 a.m., do barn chores, run, eat, then go back to the barn again. Halfway through the summer I just want to be back at college. The farm chores have now become this repetitive cycle that is wearing me out mentally and emotionally. Some days I'd unload a hay wagon in the morning instead of late afternoon, or I'd mow the lawn, but for the most part not much changes from each day. As the summer drags on, my thoughts of, I don't want to be here, I don't want to do this anymore, become louder and louder. I hate the farm. I don't want to work anymore. I can't handle this. I'm running each day, but it doesn't seem to be helping me cope as it did before.

I'm so exhausted and I just want to crawl under my covers and not wake up. I force myself each morning to get out of bed, but it becomes harder and harder. My only motivation to get up in the morning is my obedience to my dad and mom. They are expecting me to be out there working, I don't want to let them down, and maybe this time they will give me money for next semester.

My mind is not healthy. Why am I even here? I laid on the hardwood floor next to my bed, sobbing. *I can't take any more of this.* I held the empty bottle in my hands, Hydroxycut. I took the entire bottle. Pill by pill I swallowed them all. I started taking these diet pills freshman year, using the money from my babysitting jobs over the summer. Deep down I knew it wasn't going to kill me, but a part of me wanted it to. I prayed I wouldn't wake up. *No one will miss me anyway. Please God, just let it be my time.*

Why did he take Nancy and not me? I am miserable. Why didn't I get leukemia instead of her? These questions repeated in my mind. The answer was always the same: Keep going, you have things to do here. It will get better. I rolled my eyes at that voice whispering to me. What

things? I thought angrily. I fell asleep, praying I didn't
wake up.

Beep, beep, beep. I rolled over and hit the alarm. *Ugh, I'm
alive, I'm breathing.* It didn't work, but deep down I knew it
wouldn't. This feeling of shame came over me. *Why did I do
that?* I laid there with a god-awful stomachache instead,
my heart pounding like it was coming out of my chest. The
taste of the chalky pills still lingered. The thought of
swallowing another pill made me cringe, so I laid in a ball
crying and my stomach pain intensified. My anxiety
increased as I recalled what I did the night before. My
thoughts drowned me. *How could you do that? You're such a
baby, toughen up. What is wrong with you?*

I forced myself out of bed, hunching over in pain as I
dragged myself downstairs. My mom was standing in the
kitchen. She could tell by my posture that I didn't feel well.
"Mom, I need to go back to bed, my stomach hurts." She
motioned for me to go back to bed and hugged me. I curled
up under the covers and cried myself to sleep.

*Why am I feeling this way? What should I do? Do I tell
someone? No, I'll run instead, I'll just keep running.* Running
the next day, I felt heavy and slow with each step. I became
worried that missing one day of running would set me
back. I tried to pick up the pace, but I couldn't. My mind
recalling what I did, and guilt consumed me. I felt terrible.
Just keep running, I thought to myself. *Run it off.* It was the
only way I knew how to cope and pretend I was okay. I

didn't say anything. I kept quiet, and I carried this pain and shame alone. Yet I wasn't really alone. God was with me. The verse *Philippians 4:13* entered my mind: "I can do all things through Christ who strengthens me." I memorized this bible verse as a child. Any time life got hard, I would come back to this verse. I know it was God, reminding me He was there, He wouldn't leave me or give up on me. I wanted to give up, but that verse was linked to happy memories, and it would enter my mind just when I needed it.

It was summer camp where I memorized that bible verse. Memories of swimming, conquering ropes courses, hiking, laughing, camping out under the stars, praying, and singing together by the campfire all flashed in my mind. I met some great friends who became my pen pals over the school year until I saw them again the next summer. Writing letters each week kept my spirits up, and letters in the mail addressed to me gave me so much joy. I was happy. This memory made me realize that I wasn't going to be able to do life without Him. I need to stop running from God and start running with Him.

***

When I transferred my sophomore year, I met my favorite person in the world, Laughter. That is her real name and it's the perfect name for her. She was everything I wanted to be. Confident, funny, always smiling, and had no problem using her voice. We became best buddies and teammates. She knew how to have fun. I loved that running brought us together.

Junior year we became roommates. I felt like I was turning a corner. I wasn't binging and purging as often as before. I was starting to believe that I was likable. I had this weird habit of always mumbling something or muttering to myself. Laughter would inquire, "What did you say? Are you talking to me?" Oh! I was so surprised that someone was paying attention or would care what I had to say. I replied, "I'm just talking to myself." I did want to sit and talk with her about all this shit in my head. I wanted to share all these thoughts, feelings, and pain but I didn't. I didn't think this was stuff you shared with anyone, especially a friend like Laughter. I didn't want to scare her away. I continued to hide my pain. My senior year I had to find a cheaper place to live, which meant I would no longer live with Laughter.

Goofy running buddies are the BEST

I regret that I didn't somehow find the money to stay with her. She was a fantastic person to be around, it took some focus away from my thoughts about food and being thin. But my self-sabotage would get in the way, it was always getting in the way. I didn't know how to stop it. That's why living in a 600-square-foot space with another guy was no problem for me at all. *I don't need much. I can afford this.* The place was dark and musty smelling with two small windows. I was living in a bunker. If depression had a home this would have been it. My thoughts were creating these awful results in my life, and this was one of them.

I would turn down opportunities with my friends and tell myself I deserved to be alone. My logic was that I had schoolwork to do or cleaning (that place took a long time to clean) or running. *I'm not allowed to have fun or play, don't be lazy.* I didn't know that I could let these thoughts go, that I could have fun and relax. I didn't always have to be doing or working but I didn't know-how.

My belief continued that if I was thinner, I would run faster and that would change everything in my life. I would feel worthy, lovable, and good enough. I would be happy. I continued running on the team and my poor eating habits resumed, five saltine crackers, one orange, and a few diet pills. Yet I didn't see much change. I just kept looking at myself thinking, *You are so fat and disgusting.* It was an awful thing I was doing to my body, but I couldn't stop it. I would tell myself, *Don't do it,* but then a bag of M&Ms later

I would be in the bathroom because that couldn't stay in my body. I would get fat. During the cross-country season, the coaches would give us money as part of our team allowance for food. Instead of spending it on lunch, I would save it so I could buy more diet pills.

Being thin was all I focused on. It became more important than friendships, my teammates, and classes. Sometimes I would just stay in bed and not leave my room. Other times I would eat until the fullness engulfed me entirely and there was nothing left but my tears.

I continued to run on the team, though I was starting to get the sense that I didn't belong. I was running the best I could, but the stomach pain was getting worse, and it started to affect my training and racing. I wasn't eating properly, and the mouth sores were a continued nuisance. I didn't know how to cope with the intense emotions I was shoving down, so my body was letting me know. I ignored it.

I overheard some of the girls on the team make comments that I hadn't trained over the summer or that I wasn't working hard enough. That wasn't true. I did every workout the coaches gave us over the summer. Well, except that one day. You know the story. I wanted to die, but God had other plans. It was hard to see at the time, but the pain was strangling me. It was easy to think, *I don't want to live anymore, I can't take this anymore.* The horrible memory of what I attempted to do just a few months ago flashed in my mind. I wanted to forget it.

***

Outdoor track season is beginning. I was trying out steeplechase for the first time, excited to challenge myself in a new way. I thought maybe I could be good at this. Steeplechase is a 3,000-meter race around the track, jumping over four large, fixed obstacles, think hurdle but much bigger, with a water pit at the back turn of the track. It was hard, but my mind had something else to focus on during the laps around the track. I found myself not as bored. I was gaining more confidence with steeplechase, as my times at the meets improved. I was happy to not be the girl who trips or falls into the water pit. Or the last runner to come in.

When our race went off, everyone flocked over to watch. I thought spectators were hoping to see one of us fall in the water or crash into each other. It certainly would make the sport more exciting — as long as it wasn't me. This race I will forever remember, as I was the girl in her yellow race tank top to fall face-first into the water. I was so embarrassed as the water exposed my bare skin even more. My top sucked to my chest. *Grr*, I just wanted to run off the track, but I had two laps to go. I fell behind. The front pack of runners pulled ahead. I was all by myself, feeling like everyone's eyes were glued to me. The sound of my sneakers squishing with every stride annoyed the crap out of me. As I crossed the finish line, I rushed off the track to go change.

The warm rush of shame smothers me as my chest tightens. My stomach clenches up as I take off the wet singlet, wishing it never happened. I replay in my mind what I did wrong. What I should've done instead. I'm so stupid, I don't even want to face my team, I wish I could disappear. I'm terrible at this sport. I try to catch my breath but I'm so humiliated. My mind is critical and mean.

A few days later I woke up with a terrible pain in both my Achilles tendons (the tendon connecting the calf muscles to the heel). I could hardly walk, so I limped as I got ready for class. Putting my sneakers on hurt too much so I wore my Adidas flip-flops. The backs of my heels are so tender and sore. How was I going to run today in practice?

At practice I let my coaches know about my discomfort. I told them I didn't think I could run today and that I might need to take a day off. They ignored me and made me go out on the track for practice anyway. They didn't seem to think it was a problem. I was pissed. I thought, *Okay I'll show them.* I knew my legs weren't going to like this, but I guess this was the only way to let them know I wasn't faking or lying. I was angry that they didn't listen to me. *Don't they know me by now? I'm not a slacker. I work hard. I would not make this up to get out of practice.*

I started running the track, pain shooting in my heels and calf muscles. My running form changed to fend off the pain. It didn't help. My body had enough. I immediately collapsed on the track, grabbing the backs of my legs. *Well, this will get my coach's attention since my words weren't enough.* The pain was intense. I needed help getting up from the track. It got their attention. They sent me to the trainers.

The trainer had me take off my shoes, socks and sit in an ice bath for ten minutes. It was probably a good idea not only for the pain but to cool me down emotionally, force me to focus on my breath. I wanted to scream, placing each leg into the ice bath. *Those dang coaches, why didn't they listen to me! Why didn't I say no?* I tried to stay calm, focus on my breathing, and not freak out. I was mad at myself.

For the next few weeks, practice sessions consisted of ultrasound, Celebrex, ice, taping, and me beating myself up. I missed the rest of the season. The trainers believed the pain was caused by the steeplechase fall and overuse, but both my legs? I'm sure that was a factor. I believe my overall health was, too. I was being treated for physical pain in my legs only. What about the other parts of me? The social, emotional, and environmental factors were dismissed. The focus was on where the pain was and not me as a whole person. The biology, psychology, and social factors matter to all of us. The interactions between them determine our health.

What was going on in my mind would affect my body, and vice versa. My negative self-talk, not fueling my body properly, not being seen or heard by my coaches certainly were contributors. I lost trust in my coaches. When I came back my senior year to run for them, it became clear to me that I didn't belong.

***

In my senior year of college, one of my professors approached me and said, "It looks like you're having a tough time." I shrugged, looked down, and said nothing. What I wanted to say was, "YES. Please help me, I'm so messed up. I don't know what to do!" Instead, I stayed silent. I coped by running, avoiding friends, and continued the binge-purging cycle. My shame and guilt consumed me. I told my coaches I wasn't going to run on the team. I made up a lie, saying I wanted to run on my own and it was getting to be too much for me. I wanted them to beg me to stay or to help me out of this hole I was in. I didn't know how to ask for help so I quit the team.

I was in a dark place, and I was making my world smaller. I would run alone, no longer with my teammates. I thought it was better this way. I won't be a bother. I tried talking to a therapist, but I had a bad experience and I left. I never went back. *What is wrong with me?* This thought echoed in my mind. I felt helpless. As my pain, the great protector, would wake, I would run to try and escape it. I didn't want to face it. *Why won't it go away?* I screamed, *What is wrong with me!* I ignored my pain once again. It's been protecting me since childhood, whispering to me, nudging me, but I wasn't listening. I didn't want to. The rules were to ignore it, to keep going, to hide it, and pretend everything is fine. *I don't want to bother anyone. I don't want to burden anyone with my troubles. I can figure this out on my own*, I reasoned.

I was falling apart. I had to do something, but what? I recalled one of my happiest memories of running, finishing the Walt Disney World Marathon my senior year of high school. I recalled the feeling of joy, pride, doing something hard, and the courage to train for consecutive months. It was at this moment that I remembered my dream to run the Boston Marathon. *That's what I'll do. I will train for a marathon. I will qualify for Boston. That will get me out of bed every morning.* I had a new purpose, something else to focus on other than my self-hatred. I found a 16-week training plan and printed it out. I was going to follow it exactly and qualify for Boston.

I registered for the Nissan Buffalo Marathon. It was scheduled a few weeks after graduation, perfect timing. The plan after graduation was to move in with my boyfriend and work at a gym. This would be the perfect marathon to train for. I was determined to achieve my dream. I would eat better and train smarter so I could run the distances required. When I looked at my training plan, there were a few 20-mile runs scheduled. I knew I could do it. The rest of my senior year was focused on schoolwork and training for the Nissan Buffalo Marathon. My dream of getting to Boston was alive again.

Chapter Six
My Dream

Running on the roads
To qualify for Boston
Don't let up your dream

The Boston Marathon is world-famous; it's the queen of marathons. The more I read the stories of Roberta "Bobbi" Gibb, Kathrine Switzer, and the history of the race, the more I wanted to run it. The catch was that I had to qualify, and at the time I needed a 3:40:00 to run at Boston. That means running 26.2 miles in 3 hours and 40 minutes. That seemed a little out of reach for me, considering I ran my first marathon in over four hours.

The story of Kathrine Switzer influenced me the most. She entered the Boston Marathon at a time when women were not allowed to run in marathons. They thought women were not capable of running that distance, that we were too fragile or something. How ridiculous! She trained her butt off in Syracuse, N.Y., I might add, and in April 1967 she pinned on bib number 261 and toed the line. She was the only woman at the start among the men runners.

She fought for women's running. Her courage to toe the line and keep running to the finish despite her being shoved and pulled in the beginning miles is badass! I love what she was quoted saying in an interview: "I realized that if I quit this race, which I felt for a split second like doing because I was so scared and embarrassed," she said, "if I quit that race, nobody would've believed women deserved to be there or that they could do the distance. And I said, "Arnie, I'm going to finish this race on my hands and my knees if I have to."

What guts and courage to keep going despite the adversity she was up against! She made a ruckus for us women. She paved the way. I was going to run it too! Her story motivated and inspired me. I would train and work hard to get the 3:40:00 time I needed.

Bobbi Gibb was the first female to run Boston. She didn't have a bib number, but she showed up for women and ran! She hid behind the bushes, watched the pack of men go past, then made her way into the race. The race official didn't see her, and she ran among the men runners, many of them excited to see a woman running alongside them.

I love what Tom Derderian wrote about her in his book Boston Marathon: The History of the World's Premier Running Event.

"Bobbi Gibb was an artist. When she looked out from behind her bushes she saw in the stream of runners a stream of consciousness, not a race, not a competition. She slipped into the stream to join that consciousness, to be a part of the whole, not to prove anything political or to beat men at their own game, but to play." He went on to quote her writing, "My outrage turned to humor as I thought how many preconceived prejudices would crumble when I trotted right along for 26 miles."

Woot to Bobbi Gibb, how amazing and brave she was too! I love that she wanted to play, be a part of this racing tradition and experience. I wanted that too: no pressure, just run and have fun! She was reminding me why I started to run in the first place.

The Nissan Buffalo Marathon arrived, and I was ready. I had stuck to my training plan over the last four months, and for the first time was thankful to my body for staying healthy physically. When I toed the start line that morning, my excitement overwhelmed me as I was surrounded by so many runners. *I get to run; I get my chance today to qualify for Boston!*

We jumped up and down to stay warm as the sun was hiding behind the clouds, awaiting the gun to go off. My stomach fluttered as I thought about the pace I was determined to run. *I can do this. I'm ready.* We all huddled closer as we heard, "Runners, on your marks." *BANG! Here we go!*

I imagined I was Katherine Switzer and Bobbi Gibb among the men runners as I headed into the first two miles. I then spotted two women just ahead of me, lean and muscular, each wearing a fancy singlet with matching shorts. I felt great and wanted to catch up with them. If I could run with them, I could get to Boston. I was pushing myself to stay at their pace, matching their stride and breathing.

At mile 13 I felt like I was going to pass out. I patted my shorts, checking for my energy gel that was tucked away in my pocket. I grabbed it out and sucked it down. I felt this immediate surge of energy. I wanted to stay with the leading women runners. At mile 18 I started to lose steam. I had to back off. Another runner came alongside me and encouraged me. It was perfect timing. I was starting to worry I was running too slow. My mind was starting to spiral, *I'm not on pace.* I told him I wanted to qualify for Boston, and he said, "You're doing great, you will, you have a great pace." I was so happy to hear that, because I had slowed down a bit and wasn't able to stick with the pace of the other women. He said, "You're right on track for the BQ (Boston Qualifier), keep running your race." My body relaxed immediately, and a smile came on my face. I stuck with him the rest of the way, enjoying his company and encouragement. His reassurance changed my mindset and focus. *I'm right on pace. I can do this.*

As the finish line came into view, we picked up our stride. The crowd cheers fueled us in the last stretch. As I crossed the line, I stopped my watch and the time amazed me! WOOHOO! I did it, I qualified for Boston! I ran 3:28:07. For the first time, I felt a sense of belonging and pride, something I had been missing. Boston Marathon, here I come!

***

I was on a high and thought nothing could touch me. I kept right on training after the Buffalo Marathon and didn't take a break. I signed up for another marathon five months away. I loved the feeling of racing with others and the sense of belonging. I wanted to keep that going. It also helped me cope with my pain. I could keep the hurt shoved down better if I was running and had a goal. I believed running was all I needed to forget about my worries and keep going. *I can handle it.*

I continued to work at the gym, run, and focus on my training. When I ran the Casino-Niagara Marathon, my body was very uncomfortable the entire race and my stomach didn't feel well. I still finished at a respectable time, but not to my standards. I didn't rest the next day. I went out for a run. *The Boston Marathon is in six months. I need to keep training.* After my run, I went to the gym to try my first spinning class. I thought it would be fun. I was becoming friends with the instructor, and she'd been asking me to try it out. I didn't think it would be a big deal to join a spin class right after running a marathon.

I hopped on the spin bike and noticed this burning, prickling sensation and achiness at the outside of my right knee. I ignored it and kept going. The sensations got stronger. I brought my intensity down a bit on the bike but didn't stop. There were so many of us in the class that I didn't want to bring any attention to myself by stopping or leaving. I kept pushing through the pain instead. After the class, my knee hurt, and I felt this intense sensation on the outside of my knee as I walked. I was limping to my car. *I better ice it when I get home.* I was uncomfortable and took a few days off from running. I didn't go back to spin class. *The spin bike caused this knee pain. I'm not going to do that again.*

I dismissed the fact that I'd just broken up with my boyfriend for the second time. I recently finished a marathon, and my negative self-talk and poor relationship with food continued. I was not healthy but didn't believe that these things mattered or were a factor in my knee pain. I blamed it all on the spin bike. The sensation in my knee wouldn't let up, and running was becoming harder and harder. I refused to listen. I wouldn't stop. The Boston Marathon was the goal. My training continued, yet my knee was not 100 percent.

***

A month into training I was out for a run when the outside of my right knee started to ache. I ignored it like I've been doing since the spin bike class. *BOOM.* The pain brought me to my knees. I got back up and tried to run again, but it wouldn't allow me. The pain was so intense. I could feel it on the right side of my leg; the burning, prickly sensation was back. I began to limp. I was surprised that I couldn't just "walk it off."

This went on for weeks. Every time I went out for a run, the pain stopped me. I would walk instead, trying not to limp, but it was difficult. I was starting to worry because the pain was lingering longer into my days. Sitting and standing were becoming difficult. The pain was commanding my attention and focus most minutes of the day. It was exhausting. I was getting nervous. The Boston Marathon was four months away, and the pain was not allowing me to run at all. I finally went to see a doctor. I had to do something.

Chapter Seven
My Pain

Pain

My great protector

Burning, tingling, stinging

Telling me something

Discomfort

Have you ever been told to stop doing something you loved? Something that gave you so much joy and freedom? It would be like me telling my children to stop playing outside, climbing trees, or riding bikes.

This is what happened to me. I was told to stop doing something I loved.

The doctor said, "You can't run. It's your iliotibial band. You have to stop running. Do something else." I bit my lip and stared at the hard linoleum floor. My stomach clenched as the words, "You can't run," registered in my brain.

He simply said it and left the room. My mind raced, I'm running the Boston Marathon in four months! This can't be happening. Are you serious? Now, what am I supposed to do? My mind was desperate to figure this out.

My dream of running Boston was now being taken away from me. I couldn't believe it. *I have to run.* It was my stress reliever. It was my Prozac. Running made me feel free, strong, and in charge. It brought me so much joy. I finally was feeling a sense of belonging and now my body was telling me no.

I sat alone in the small, cold office, my face in my hands. My stomach ached. My chest tightened as tears welled up in my eyes. My inner critic showed up. She didn't say what you would say to a friend. She was mean, loud, and convincing. *You aren't good at running anyway. You need to lose weight; you are too fat. You're disgusting. Forget about Boston, it's too hard.*

Of course, I felt defeated, frustrated, and alone — look at my thoughts. But as I sat in that doctor's office, I had no clue that my thoughts even mattered. I didn't know that my thoughts were a choice. The one thing that I had complete control over!

I wish I knew that in 2003. All I knew was I would have to wait on my dream. My attention would now be on this pain and how to get rid of it. I left the doctor that day in tears.

***

I applied and was accepted into D'Youville College to earn a doctorate in physical therapy. During this time, my studies were my main focus, though my pain was still seeking my attention. I didn't have health insurance, so I didn't pursue any care. I figured it would eventually go away or I would figure it out myself. This was, after all, the main reason I went back to school: to figure out my pain. I was determined to run the Boston Marathon.

I was living in the dorms when I spotted a sign-up sheet offering free 30-minute massage therapy sessions. I jumped on that and signed up immediately. Maybe this would help me, and I would be back to running in no time. When I went to see him, it was a miracle. I told him it was my knee but for some reason, he knew something I didn't because he was rubbing my glute, back, and right hip. This was increasing my knee pain! How did he know? I could feel the tingling, burning sensations, but the more he worked on these areas, the better my knee started to feel. I was so surprised that my knee was hurting when he worked on my back area. He connected it all for me: The knee symptoms and leg sensations were all coming from my back. I felt relief and hope, but I had so many questions. I wanted to know more. *Okay, so it's my back, not my knee or iliotibial band.* He offered his services to me, but at the time I didn't have the money. When I left there, I didn't have any knee pain. I figured the problem was solved.

I was happy to have some relief — finally. I guess it was all muscle tightness in my back, that's what he said. He also mentioned my sciatic nerve, hmm, I will keep that in my mind as I learn more in my classes. I'm going for a run tomorrow. Woohoo!

To lace up my running sneakers again, get on the roads and explore the area where I was living was what I wanted most. I loved that about running; anytime and anywhere, I could take off, leaving all my worries behind me. The next day I went out to run. I was huffing and puffing. It had been over a year since I had run. I was out of shape. My legs were already burning, and it had only been five minutes. My breathing was labored, my pace slow. *I have some work to do*, I thought, as the Boston Marathon came into my mind. I hadn't forgotten, and I was determined to achieve it.

I ran two miles that day, with a slight sensation at the outside of my right knee. The discomfort came back, but nothing like it was before. I was running! I was determined to keep running this time and now that I was in physical therapy school, I was hopeful. I started increasing my miles. As my mileage went up, so did my knee pain — and my back hurt, along with a burning sensation in my right hip. It got louder. It wasn't getting better, so I backed down the mileage again. I mentioned something to my professor during one of our classes. He suggested a cortisone injection for my knee. "That may help you." I told him I didn't have insurance to cover that. He said this would be free. I failed to mention my back pain, sciatic nerve, or what happened when the massage therapist worked on me.

I ignored the other parts of my body and didn't trust myself. I took his offer of a free injection instead. I pushed down my gut feeling that this wasn't a good idea. This wasn't a knee problem.

I was a little nervous heading into the school's training room, where the cortisone shot would be given. It was a very small room, with one table to sit on and the doctor sitting on a stool waiting for me. I walked in and took a seat. I pointed to the outside of my right knee where I was having the majority of the pain. He took out the needle, longer than I expected, as he came closer to insert it in my knee I looked away and closed my eyes. I felt this very strong stingy and burning sensation as the cortisone went into my knee. I pretended I was fine, but it hurt more than when I came in. I got off the table and was limping. The doctor saw my concern and immediately reassured me that the pain would go away, just give it a day or two. A week later I was still limping. I quit my part-time job because I couldn't stand at the register. It was too painful. *Those concrete floors must be the problem.*

I was so frustrated and angry. He told me the pain would go away. Why didn't it?! I began to ruminate and blame myself. I should not have gotten the shot. Why did I do that? Why didn't I listen to my gut? This isn't your knee, Julie, it's something else. I should have told my professor about my back pain too. I was spiraling down, beating myself up, and my pain was not improving. The worst part was I had to stop running again.

One day in orthopedic physical therapy class we got into groups and began practicing some of the tests on each other. We were learning how to assess the sacroiliac joint and what tests to perform on a patient if we thought this was the problem. I remember being tested on the right side (where I was having all my trouble). They determined from the tests that my sacroiliac joint was rotated. I was excited to learn this! *Maybe I can fix this. I'll be back to running in no time.*

My professor set me up with a physical therapist close to the college. The physical therapist confirmed that it was my sacroiliac joint causing all my symptoms. He didn't mention anything about my sciatic nerve or back, so I believed it was my sacroiliac joint, not my back, not my iliotibial band or knee. He taught me some movements to help myself as well as strengthening exercises to get me back to running. I did them religiously.

I began to run a little more each week. I still felt sensation in my back and right leg, but it wasn't enough to stop me from running. I was so happy my body was letting me run again. It wasn't perfect, but it was progress, so I didn't complain. I didn't have any more physical therapy sessions left, so I kept up with what he gave me on my own. It seemed to be the answer, as I was running a little more than before. I breathed a sigh of relief. *I know what to do now to help myself.* That thought didn't last long. Some days I could run for two miles, other days four miles. The pain would move and change from day to day. Sometimes my knee would ache and burn. Other days, it was fine, and it would be my hip/back bothering me. It was exhausting and frustrating.

I thought I had understood my pain. Why was it still there, even with all the strengthening and specific movements I was told to do? I was given so many explanations for why I hurt, I didn't know what to believe. Is the pain because of running, is it my sacroiliac joint, my back, the sciatic nerve, or all of them? It was very frustrating. I ignored the physical discomfort as best I could. I would run each day, still not feeling healthy or strong. I was not taking care of myself. The thought loop continued, *What's wrong with me? Why do I still have this pain? What did I do wrong?*

I pretended I was fine. Deep down I was not. I wasn't running the miles I wanted to. A marathon is 26.2 miles. I was only running two to four miles three or four times a week. How would I ever get back to running a marathon? It seemed like an impossible goal for me, even though I had done it before. I couldn't stop ruminating. My mind was running wild. I didn't know where to turn for help, so just shoved it all down. I continued to trudge along, carrying a backpack of burdens that were getting heavier with every step. I didn't want to look inside. I wasn't ready to unpack all the unresolved emotional and physical pain. I only knew to keep running. That is what I did best. It was how I coped.

I managed to graduate with a doctorate in physical therapy, carrying my enormous backpack with me. As I stood in front of my family, friends, and teachers to receive my diploma, my eyes stared down toward my feet, cowering at what I'd accomplished. Past conversations rattled my mind. *Are you ever going to be done with school? Why do you need to get your doctorate?* I couldn't be proud of myself or happy with what I have achieved. This was an old story from childhood that I'm not able to let go of. *When can I be proud of myself? When will I let this old story go?*

Chapter Eight
My Wake-Up Call

My skin was a sign
Please get help, no more hiding
What's out of balance?

I was nine months into my career as a physical therapist. I was hanging on to a relationship that wasn't working yet planning a wedding. My body was telling me to slow down. I was not listening.

I had just come back from a continuing education course, an eight-hour road trip. I woke up the next morning with excruciating low back and right hip pain. I couldn't bend over or sit. I could hardly move. I managed to get dressed, tears in my eyes as I got on my sneakers and headed to work. I was struggling, but I couldn't call in. My coworker there took a look at me and assessed my sacroiliac joint. That was her assumed diagnosis. *Again, it's my right sacroiliac joint.* This pain was excruciating, and I couldn't believe it was that, but I took her word for it. She showed me some movements to do, different movements from what I was taught in graduate school. She looked at my back and said my ribs didn't look right and began doing some joint mobilizations (gentle pushes on my ribs) to help.

I was almost in tears but shoved them down and pretended
everything was fine. I wanted to just go home, cry, and go
to bed.

As long as I stood, I was able to continue working, but
sitting was another story. It felt like someone had hit me
with a baseball bat several times, I felt so bruised and stiff.
The mental image of a baseball bat hitting me over and
over was not helpful, I realize now. I sat as still, tense, and
upright as I could. If I relaxed my spine and slouched, a
shot of pain would grab me. X-rays were taken but showed
nothing. I thought the worst. After several weeks of
suffering from the discomfort and moving very carefully,
the pain subsided on its own. Was it from the joint
mobilizations, sacroiliac joint movements, or Aleve? I had
no idea. It just stopped hurting. It was so strange, but I was
very relieved I could start running again.

I woke one morning several months later, itching the back
of my head. It hurt. When I looked in the mirror, I saw a
large flaky patch of redness covering the back of my scalp.
That's weird. How did that get there?

The same red, itching, painful patch showed up on my
elbows, knees, and tops of my feet. *What is this?* I tried to
shrug it off. It would wake me up in the middle of the
night. My head and elbows itched so badly that it was hard
to get back to sleep.

My elbows started to bleed from all my scratching. I noticed flakes of skin covering my shoulders from itching my scalp so much. I could tell my patients were disgusted. Their staring was a sure giveaway. I was becoming more and more self-conscious. It was difficult to focus on work.

My skin was something everyone could see. I couldn't hide it. I went to a dermatologist. I thought maybe it was eczema. That's what my coworkers thought. She very calmly, unconcerned, said, "No, this is psoriasis." She handed me topical creams and a special shampoo for my scalp.

I sat there and cried. I couldn't control myself; the tears wouldn't stop. She looked at me and said, "Maybe you need to talk to someone," then left the room. I felt so alone and abandoned. I recognized this feeling before. I hated it. *Why can't I keep it together? Why am I always crying? What does she mean I need to talk to someone?*

Because of my inability to keep my composure, I didn't ask any questions. I left there, unaware of what psoriasis was or what I could do to help myself other than using the creams. The self-loathing continued. I was beating the crap out of myself with my thoughts. I continued to live with my pain, not knowing who to turn to.

The psoriasis was something I could see and feel every day. It was hard to ignore. I was starting to get some relief from the scalp itching, but then a new itching started in my genital area. It was spreading all over me, it seemed. I was too embarrassed to mention this new discomfort.

I didn't know that I could improve my psoriasis by managing my stress, managing my mind (hello, crappy thoughts and rumination), proper nutrition, and regular exercise.

I wasn't aware it was an autoimmune condition or that sleep mattered. I didn't know and I didn't ask. My priority was not on what my skin was trying to tell me. I focused on the wedding invitations, the cake, and what color flowers do you want? I had no business planning a wedding, yet I didn't know how to say no.

***

I can't cancel the wedding. I can't tell everyone to go home. I stood there in the church, my stomach in knots and my chest tight. I began to panic. I wanted to run, but I couldn't disappoint everyone. What would they think of me? I have to be a good girl and do everything perfectly. I can't change my mind now.

I shoved the feelings down and ignored what my body was telling me. I walked down the aisle. It was a big mistake. I didn't listen to my courage, and I hurt a lot of people. It was my fault. My burden to now carry and add to my backpack. It was a terrible feeling. I was a liar.

I was saying yes to things when I wanted to say no. I knew this marriage wasn't for me, but everyone said it was. "You've been together for so long. It will be better when you're married." I didn't want a big wedding. I didn't want this, but everyone else did. *This is what's expected of me. I don't want to disappoint them.* I wanted his parents to like me. I just agreed and said yes. The pain inside continued.

After two and a half years of pretending it would work, my body finally said, "Enough!" It was 2009. My marriage was coming to an end. I was going through a divorce.

The pain was unbearable. The grief and despair were awful. I experienced tingling and numbness in both my legs, feet, and toes. I was having intense back pain that wouldn't allow me to sit or bend over. Do you realize how much we sit and bend over?

I was working full-time as a physical therapist in an outpatient clinic. The majority of patients came in with back pain similar to what I was experiencing. I was working on the weekends at the hospital to pay my bills. I was working seven days a week; lawyers are not cheap.

This season was difficult and disheartening. This pain came on out of nowhere. I didn't fall. I didn't have an injury. I wasn't running, but I did take a road trip for a continuing education course. Could this pain be from sitting so much? I was trying to figure out what I did wrong to cause this pain. Was it my sacroiliac joint again? It felt similar. I didn't connect it to the fact that my marriage was failing, or that I wasn't taking care of myself, or that I wasn't asking for help. My parents were struggling with the farm, and I was worried about finances.

I became a physical therapist to figure out my pain, and I was failing. I thought I knew all about pain. I didn't. If I did, I would have realized that everything matters. What was happening in my life mattered. My thoughts, beliefs, nutrition, sleep, exercise, and memories were contributing. My body did not feel safe.

I somehow got to work the next day, and my boss could see I was in pain. I couldn't hide that. I had this moment of asking, *How can I help my patients if I can't even help myself?* I started questioning my ability to even perform my job. I'd felt entitled because this job I chose would give me immunity from pain, right? I was angry at my body.

I worked in silence. Any chance I got, I walked around or did the movements I thought would help. I saw an orthopedic surgeon that week because the nerve symptoms were not letting up. I couldn't stand it anymore. The tingling and numbness in my feet and legs were wearing me out. The diagnosis was a herniated disc in my back. The doctor gave me a steroid pack for seven days to help with the nerve symptoms and sent me on my way. Another diagnosis to add to my backpack.

I couldn't sit or bend over. The pain squeezed me as I held my breath. Getting up and down from the toilet was a nightmare, a jerk of pain reminding me to move cautiously. I stared at my socks and shoes on the floor, mentally rehearsing how I would move to get them on. *I can do this; I can handle the pain.* It brought me to tears. I wanted to die. I was suffering in silence. I was almost thankful for it. I deserved it. I was getting a divorce. Was this God's way of reminding me I need him? I can't do life without him. It was a marriage that never should have happened, the red flags were there loud and clear. I'd ignored them. I was great at ignoring my voice of courage. Pleasing others and making everyone else happy were more important.

The shame was overwhelming, and I wanted to disappear. I was alone. I could just hide and deal with this pain all by myself. Who wants to be around me? I will not get married again. The hiding became a habit. The thought that I'm not lovable was my truth.

But God.

God is faithful. God had my back. He was giving me doors to walk through, and now it was up to me to trust Him, to have the courage to listen to my body, heart, and mind. I had strayed so far from God. I wasn't listening to Him or my body. What was going on in my life was the result.

My failed marriage was mile 18 in the marathon. I hit the wall; my breath knocked out of me. My backpack is too heavy to carry alone. I could give up, wallow in my self-pity and shame, or I could accept the pain, draw strength from my faith and start unpacking all that I've been carrying since childhood. This setback was my wake-up call. I would need to turn my life around and face my pain, fears, shame, and bring to light all that I had been hiding. I found the courage, patience, and persistence to keep going with God by my side.

A bible verse that I memorized as a child was *Philippians 4:13: "I can do all things through Christ who strengthens me."* I would say this verse at the barn, during a race, or during a test. Any time life got hard, I would remind myself of this verse. My faith is what kept my head above water though I felt like I was gasping for air more than I would like to admit. I kept coming back to this verse. I know it was God, reminding me He was there, He wouldn't leave me or give up on me. There were times I wanted to give up, but that verse was linked to happy memories, and it would enter my mind just when I needed it.

It was summer camp, Camp ID-RA-HA-JE (I'd rather have Jesus) where I memorized that verse. When I thought about that verse, memories of swimming, conquering ropes courses, hiking, laughing, camping out under the stars, praying, and singing together by the campfire all flashed in my mind. I met some great friends, my pen pals over the school year until I saw them again the next summer. Writing letters each week kept my spirits up, and letters in the mail addressed to me gave me so much joy. I was happy. This memory made me realize that I wasn't going to be able to do life without Him. I would need God's strength to face this long journey ahead. I would need to choose faith over fear.

Chapter Nine
Loss and Grief

Let it go
not your path
it's time to heal
to be you
God has a plan

I was on the farm the day the auction started. My parents were selling the tractors, equipment, and the entire farm. There were a lot of people there, and I heard what people were saying. A woman came up to me whom I didn't know. The conversation went something like this: "Does your dad own a gun?"

"No, why?"

"Well, your dad is losing his farm, I know many farmers who have taken their lives over the loss."

I couldn't believe she was talking about this with me. I stood there, looking at her with my arms folded across my chest in shock. My mind started freaking out, *No, he doesn't have a gun. He wouldn't do that. I better talk to Mom about this. Where is she? Oh my gosh, would he kill himself!?*

My body started to respond to this conversation. My stomach was in knots, I could feel myself shaking inside and my chest tightening. I didn't even know who this woman was, but she seemed so concerned for my dad, I felt that I should be too.

She pleaded with me. "Make sure you keep an eye on your dad. Make sure he isn't alone."

I began to panic.

"What is he going to do when the farm's gone?" I asked.

My mom said, "He is driving down to Tennessee to see your brother and staying there. I'm not sure when he is coming back."

"Mom, will he be okay by himself? Why are you not going?"

"He wants to be alone," is all she said and walked away. She didn't want to talk to me about it and I didn't push. This heaviness came over me and I felt nauseous.

The auctioneer began the bidding process as I looked around to make sure my dad was still there. He was talking to some other farmers and my mom stood with some woman from church. I trudged over to where my mom was listening to the auctioneer as he rattled off the bidding. A few men raised their bidder cards. I felt surrounded by the overwhelming whispers from the crowd.

I felt tremendous sadness and guilt come over me as items were sold. Soon enough, the farm was next. The sadness surprised me because I thought it was a good thing my parents were finally selling. The farm seemed like such a burden, with constant financial and emotional stress. It was at the brink of bankruptcy, and the hardships of finding a reliable hired hand to help was difficult. The guilt of not wanting to take over the farm also consumed me. I didn't want this life, but I could sense deep down that my dad had wanted one of us to take over the farm. I was the only one of their children there and felt this weight hanging on me. My mind interrogated me. *Why didn't you stay on the farm? You could have turned this around, turned it into an organic farm. You could have grown fruit, too.*

Oh, brain, I see you, but you know why we didn't stay. I've seen too much and endured so much pain. I don't have to choose this life anymore. As much as I hated the farm, I was sad to see it go. So much happened there, good, and bad of course, but my childhood was that farm. That's where we built hay forts, jumped off from the lofts into a huge mound of sawdust and searched for baby kittens. We had epic sledding in the winter and ice skating down by the pond. In the summer, we would run through the rows of corn, the green stalks hitting my bare arms, the sound of the dirt under my feet. Sometimes I would stand in the middle of the field, the corn now taller than me, making me invisible. I would listen to the wind, the birds, the cars passing by, and cows mooing. It was a place to escape. It was peaceful. If you ever get a chance to walk through a cornfield, do it. It is the best feeling.

We watched baby calves being born, which was a miracle to see at such a young age. I would contribute by sticking a piece of straw in their nose as soon as they entered the world. Are they breathing? Are they alive? I would squat over the calf to make sure, with my eyes wide. As I got older, we would help by pulling the rope to assist the cow in pushing her baby out. We tied little ropes to the calves' legs sticking out of the mother, then a large rope tied to that, this one we used to pull. I felt pride and happiness as I participated in a miracle happening right before my eyes. I was helping this cow. It was an overwhelming feeling of joy.

These were the moments when fear was invisible. These were all my joys of the farm. These are the ones I choose to remember now. Though I can't forget all the pain the farm caused, I understand it. I'm grateful. I can see how these moments kept the pain from consuming me completely.

***

I was sick of talking to myself in such a mean way and listening to it. I wanted to feel better. Thank goodness my 29-year-old-self dumped her ego and went to a therapist.

I walked into her small, cozy office. The window was open, and there was a nice breeze coming in. My stomach ached a bit as I sat down in the chair across from her. I placed my lumbar support behind my back, hoping I could sit the entire session. Sitting was not my favorite thing to do. The longer I sat, the more my back ached.

This was my second try at therapy. My first therapist fell asleep while I was talking, so I left. Maybe this therapist would be more attentive. I was doubtful, yet desperate for help. Her voice was pleasant and warm. I felt a little more relaxed as the session started. I began with my divorce, it was fresh. *I'm worried, anxious, and scared. This isn't how I wanted my life to go. It's such a mess. I am a mess.*

Of course, I didn't want to dig deep into the childhood pain and experiences, but that's where we had to start. *UGH.* This was hard work for sure, but I stuck with it. I came back to her office every week, feeling more relaxed and safer. It became easier to open up to her about my past. I had no idea all the hurt and pain I was carrying inside. I feel lighter, a little clearer every week. Here is where I could let it all out without judgment or criticism. I felt safe. I felt heard. There were a lot of tears. I had so much anger inside me, but I was finally getting it out. It was forcing me to not hide anymore. I no longer had to pretend like everything was okay. I was not okay. I have not been okay for a very long time. My body was telling me, and I was finally ready to listen.

I didn't know how to talk about my emotions. *What am I feeling?* My therapist encouraged me to start exploring my feelings and permitted me to feel them. I noticed that feeling these feelings and talking with her about all the pain I was holding onto increased my back symptoms. The nerve pain came back. I called it nerve pain. The numbness and tingling in my feet and this weird sting at the outside of my right knee, then my left knee. These sensations would move around. I thought it was from the herniated disc. I still had this belief that the disc was the cause of my symptoms. But when I felt it as I was sitting in her office, I couldn't make sense of it. It was so weird. It would get louder, softer, then go away. What is going on? The therapy sessions were intense. I was in tears most of the time and emotionally drained. I was facing many painful moments in my life that I never talked about. My nervous system was on high alert, and that was why the volume of my symptoms had gone up.

I was sitting on the couch in her office when my back would tense up, and I'd feel a weird stinging sensation at my left knee, then my right knee. I felt like I had a rock in my shoe when I didn't. So odd, and yet normal for me. The pain would wax and wane during our sessions and into the next day. This is how it showed up in my body. This was my pain experience. Once I accepted this as my body's way of telling me something is out of balance, I could breathe. I could let this idea go that my spine was fragile and weak. I could shift my focus from the herniated disc to what I could do to get healthier and to gain a balance. I didn't want to continue with therapy, yet it was exactly where I needed to be. It was the work I needed to do. I wanted a better life. It was up to me, and I trusted that God would be with me. My courage was with me and my verse during this time, *Philippians 4:13*, replayed in my mind. I was on my way to healing by looking inward and bringing light to all the darkness.

As my marriage was coming to an end, my parents decided theirs was ending too. They had sold the farm and, maybe in the loss and grief, my parents had nothing left for each other. It was a confusing and difficult season. I was in therapy at the time trying to figure myself out. My childhood was shining a light on a lot of why things unraveled as they did. *No wonder why I'm in pain.* I wasn't going to be able to heal unless I stepped away. I couldn't help my parents. It was my time to help myself. This was the hardest part of my recovery because not many people could understand. I had to remember my truth and change my direction. I did not want to repeat the past. Instead of running away from God, I ran towards him to help me process the pain, shame, and guilt I was carrying.

It felt so good to share what I had hidden for so long with my therapist. I felt lighter after each session. My body was not as tense, my pain not as loud. I found my running to be getting easier. I was running longer. God, therapy, and running were guiding me through this difficult season. I was glad that my body was healing so I could get back to running. My pain was connected to the old story I was carrying since childhood. It was time to let it go.

***

I recall one of my therapy sessions during my divorce. We were talking about my people-pleasing tendencies. My entire life, up until now, has been what people have told me to do. I never stopped to consider that I don't have to do what they are suggesting or what they want. I'm an adult, after all.

It was easier to people-please, though. I didn't have to hurt them or deal with the conflict that I was certain would happen. I ignored my pain instead. I reasoned that I wouldn't know how to handle the yelling or the disappointment. My guilt consumed me. It was simpler this way. *I don't want to rock the boat.*

I'd been carrying around this manual since childhood and couldn't let it go. The manual of perfectionism, people-pleasing, self-hatred, I needed to set it down. That manual was outdated and not serving me anymore. It was harmful and not true. I wanted a new manual.

I kept asking myself, *Where is my courage?* I want to be able to have difficult conversations and still be loved. I want to face my inner turmoil, fear, and pain. I don't want to hide anymore or pretend. I want to be me. I want to be myself. I took a deep breath. I knew the answer after my therapy session that day. I had to throw my manual out of the boat! The narrative that I'd been telling myself had to go overboard. It was the only way I was going to heal.

This was extremely hard and painful to accept. It meant I would be paddling upstream against the unknown alone. But I wasn't alone, my courage was there in the boat with me, shining a light. He was with me and for me. He never gave up on me. He whispered, "Julie, lean on me, I'm here. I will be your strength and I will never leave you." I whispered back, "Courage, I love you, please forgive me. I need you." We grabbed hands and breathed, "Let's go chase our dream. Onward!"

Chapter Ten
The Keys to My Medicine Cabinet

My brain had the proof
Danger greater than safety
Back stiffness, can't move
Not again, tingling, numb
Stay calm, breathe, you know this pain

My belief around pain was that it meant my body was injured or there was something wrong with my structure. As a runner, hurt usually means overuse injury. *I strained a muscle, which means I'm not running the right way, or my structure is the problem.* There is a cause, then there is the effect. That's how I believed my pain experience worked. I had multiple "experts" examine my running and critique my form, from how I landed to the sneakers I wore in hopes of finding the answer to my pain challenge. My thoughts were, *I just need to change how I run, then I won't have this pain* or *Tell me what muscle is weak and I'll get stronger.*

It was frustrating because even when I would do what I was told, the pain would stay, get worse, or move around! It didn't make sense to me, and even with a degree in physical therapy I still couldn't figure it out. Just when I thought I knew what the cause was, it would show up again and I couldn't connect it with anything I did. *I didn't hurt myself, I just got out of bed. Why is this so severe at times, so intense?*

I assumed I must have done something to cause the pain, but what? I must have sat too long or slouched. Did I lift wrong or run too much this week? I must not be doing enough strengthening or I'm not doing the right strengthening. Oh I know, I need to lose more weight so that I won't hurt. All my assumptions and beliefs about my pain were wrong. There was no amount of strengthening, special sneakers, or changes to my running form that would solve what I was experiencing.

As my pain persisted, moved around, and showed up in new places, I increased my reading, researching, and questioning. I looked to the experts in hopes of finding answers, and it opened up ideas and beliefs that I didn't expect. I came across the textbook *Explain Pain* by Lorimer Moseley and David Butler, published by Noigroup Publications in 2003. It opened my eyes and challenged much of what I learned. This book began my quest for more knowledge and understanding. It required me to relearn, rethink, and question my beliefs. I had no idea the contributors to my pain experience until I got brave to look beyond what I knew and go against the status quo.

***

If I don't run anymore, will the pain stop? I was starting to question running, and if it was time to give it up and let my dream go. *What about the Boston Marathon? Don't give up on your dream.* My voice of courage urged me to keep going. I took a deep breath, and with tears in my eyes, I listened. *I don't want to give up, I love to run. I want to keep running. I'll find a way. I'll keep pushing courage.*

I reminded myself why I chose running, why I love to run. It's my time to think, let go of my worries, manage my stress, and feel free. It's my time to connect with nature: what I see, hear, and find. I have found that the longer I run, the better I feel. It's a daily practice that my body craves. People say I'm crazy to want to run marathons, but I know the truth about running — and my voice of courage reminded me. There was no way I was going to let the pain stop me, either.

It had let go for a while but running was a well inside of me that wouldn't dry up; not even the stronghold of pain could take it away from me. Running made me feel strong, confident, proud, in charge, free, and happy. It was a way to open the medicine cabinet in my brain to all of those happy hormones that we all have access to any time of day, free of charge.

The brain produces endorphins, serotonin, and even substances as strong as morphine. I learned about my medicine cabinet in a book called *The Explain Pain Handbook Protectometer* by Lorimer Moseley and David Butler,

published in 2015 by Noigroup Publications. This was my
self-help book for my pain recovery journey. The
protectometer is where I learned of DIMs (danger in me)
and SIMs (safety in me). Running was a strong safety (SIM)
for me. It was a key to open up my medicine cabinet. How
awesome is that? But I needed more keys (more safety)
during my pain challenge to help me.

The protectometer taught me that when there is more
evidence of danger than safety, then pain will likely
emerge. It was a great tool for me to start confronting my
dangers. *What are the things in my life that make me feel unsafe
or make me worry?* To start seeking more safety, I asked
What are the things in life that make me feel safe? I began to
recognize using the handbook as a guide. When I had more
DIMs than SIMs, I had more pain. The protectometer uses
seven categories to discover your danger and safety in each
one: *Things you do; Things you think and believe; People in your
life; Things you hear, see, smell, taste, or touch; Things you say;
Places you go; and Things happening in your body.* These
categories encouraged me to write down what I was hiding
and avoiding. I wrote what I wanted in my life, what I
enjoyed doing, and what made me happy.

The protectometer, writing down my SIMs (safety in me);
was the way to find more keys to open my medicine
cabinet. I asked myself: *What are the things in life that make
me feel safe? What are the things in life that make me feel happy*

and calm? I started searching. The more I found, the more keys I had.

I began writing out what the SIMs were for me in each category. The more I wrote, the bigger my world became. I was starting to find myself, to find what I wanted to do rather than what someone else was telling me to do or what I "should" do. There are so many opinions out there. I learned to stop listening to all the noise outside of me, and I turned inward. I needed to get back to listening to my body. I wanted to be an expert about me.

Writing out my SIMs was empowering. It allowed me to begin taking action. It could be as simple as sitting and smelling my coffee, writing down five things I'm grateful for, or listening to music. I could see that adding in more things that make me happy during my day was great self-care, and my attention to my pain changed. I was giving my brain evidence of safety by recognizing what my SIMs were and adding them into my week, and this shifted my focus off the pain. It was a great distractor.

Just like writing the SIMs in each category, I also needed to identify the dangers (DIMs) in each category. The dangers were easier for me to find, especially the things you say and things happening in my body. It was hard to see all my messy bits in writing, but I was giving them less power by finally bringing them out of me onto paper and confronting them. I was glad to have a therapist alongside me during this process because it's work to not be done alone.

One huge danger I wrote down under "things you do" was binge and purge. I hated to write this out. I could feel my body tense up as I held my breath. I wanted to keep it a secret, but I needed to bring this to the light. Writing it out then gave me the courage to share it with my therapist.

It felt good to finally tell someone, though shame came over me as I sat in her office and blurted it out. The conversation went something like this: "Julie, this was how you gained some control. It wasn't your fault. You were a child and doing the best you could. I'm so glad you told me."

She knew it was hard for me to say. I wanted to stop this and let it go. I was carrying so much guilt, shame, and ugliness around this behavior. This was a pretty big danger (DIM) to be carrying around in my backpack. It was contributing to my pain and felt good to confront it.

Gratefully, during the divorce, I got to keep Kole, my dog, a black lab mix. Kole was a wonderful companion during this season, just what I needed. He helped me get out of bed every morning for walks. During my pain setback, he was a big reason to keep going. I may not have walked at all if it wasn't for him. He kept me going through my sadness, pain, and grief. I would come home from work, and he would run toward me, wagging his tail, and licking my face, so happy to see me. It made me smile. I would hug him and thank God that he was mine. He would cuddle with me on the couch as I cried, his soft black head in my lap with his eyes closed, which is his way of consoling me. He knew I was hurting, and he was trying to keep me safe. Kole was my sunshine, my buddy, and he got me through some really hard seasons.

Kole, walking him morning and night, and being outside with nature was my safety (SIMs). Yet my dangers (DIMs) outweighed the safety (SIMs) during this time and was why my pain was so severe. Divorce is a huge DIM, all the stigma around it, the lawyer's fees, the splitting of items, failure, and disappointment was a dark cloud covering me. I was ruminating on what I should have done differently, why I didn't listen to my voice of courage, and why I was so messed up. The pain was going to continue unless I confronted my danger (DIMs) and explored more safety (SIMs).

The evidence was there, just like the handbook said. "You will have pain when your brain concludes that there is more evidence of danger (DIMs) than there is credible evidence of safety (SIMs)." I was way out of balance. I sat there and looked at the sticky note piles of dangers in each category compared to the one sticky note in each category of safety. It was clear to me why I was having such severe pain without an injury that I could recall. I had way too many dangers. My body's response was tingling, burning, stiffness, and the inability to run as a way to protect me until the evidence changed.

The more knowledge I gained, the more empowered I felt to face my fears, look inward, and question my beliefs. *What if this pain isn't about damage?* Then I can run, I don't have to be afraid of the pain, and I can slouch if I want. I can lift heavy things again and I can do yoga. I got curious and brave. The more I questioned, the more I was open to rethink and relearn. This allowed me to learn the truth.

***

The truth is, our brain decides if we feel pain, not our tissues. This is why my pain continued even when I stopped running. My tissues or structure wasn't the problem, even though that's what hurt. My brain still perceived I was in danger, so my pain persisted. The challenge for me was to figure out why my brain assumed I required protection. What were the dangers (DIMs) or threats I needed to confront? But most importantly, what were my strengths and safety (SIMs), how could I build on these? I was ready to find out.

This handbook sparked my curiosity. It was something I could come back to each day to keep my brain in the game. It allowed me to figure out what dangers I needed to confront and what safety to give a go at my pace. It opened my eyes to the information I had no idea existed. I was happy to be a forever student, accepting there is always more to learn. I'm grateful to Lorimer Moseley and David Butler for this life-changing Protectometer Handbook and knowledge. This is where I start my pain recovery journey. Let's go!

Chapter Eleven
The Comeback

Running is my buddy
Even when it's muddy
Some people think I'm crazy
But I wasn't born lazy
Running is for me
As far as I can see
I get to be who I am
It is my jam
I feel strong and free
YIPPEE!

I was thirty-one and determined to get back to running marathons. I was running three days a week with no huge setbacks. My back and lateral knee symptoms were quieter. I was learning movement was the best thing for me. Running was my movement of choice. I just loved how it made me feel. I felt free again!

I got into the New York City Marathon in November 2011. This would be my first marathon since October 2002.

My goal for training was to get in the mileage and not worry about speed. *I just want to finish,* was my mantra. I needed to get back to marathon distance and racing before I set my eyes again on qualifying for Boston. I needed to prove to myself that my body and mind can handle the distance. I wanted to call myself a marathoner again.

It was six long months of training, not only for my body but my mind. I wanted to get that marathon mindset. What will I say to myself when the pain comes, and I want to stop? What will I say to keep my body moving forward?

I was learning to direct my mind in the direction I wanted. They say where attention goes, energy flows. I wanted my energy to focus less on the pain. I wanted my attention focused on my breathing, positive thoughts, and the experience of the marathon.

Some thoughts I was trying on during my long runs: I am a strong runner. I am sore but safe. This pain doesn't mean damage. When the going gets tough, the tough get going. I was born to run.

It was at this time I met my husband, Jeff. Jeff is tall and thin, with kind blue eyes and light brown hair. He was very laid back and I heard many people imply that he was "the hippie doctor." I'm not sure what they meant by that, but I liked his gentle, calm demeanor. I wanted to be around him more.

Every Saturday I would do a two-to-three-hour run, and he insisted on coming. I was surprised by this. *Does Jeff* want *to come with me? Does he know I've run alone my entire life? Does he know I start at 5 a.m.?* He was not okay with me running alone, and it was strange to me that he cared. It never was a big deal to anyone else. Jeff is not a runner, but I learned he enjoys biking. He bought a bike to train with me. I was shocked and excited that he would want to hang out with me at 5 a.m. Jeff biked alongside me, handing me water along the way. The two-hour runs seemed like 30 minutes as we chatted about sports, growing up, and work. I was laughing and running again. I was so glad to have him with me as I got my running legs back. I felt like my life was finally going in the right direction.

Our relationship grew on that trail every Saturday morning at 5 a.m. This time together increased my trust in him. Jeff was someone I could count on. He showed up every morning to bike as I ran even in the rain. He stuck with me.

The day before the marathon Jeff gave me a gift, a book *Second Wind: One Woman's Midlife Quest to Run Seven Marathons on Seven Continents* by Cami Ostman. I smiled as I opened the front cover to find a note that he wrote to me. As I began to read, my eyes filled with tears. His words were about me. They were kind, encouraging, and like nothing I was used to.

I had a hard time believing that anyone thought of me this way. The story I'd believed since childhood was that I wasn't lovable, I didn't matter, and that I wasn't worthy. *Jeff says the opposite.*

I wanted to believe what he wrote. I want to be loved.
Another thought came into my consciousness. But Julie,
they say you can't be loved until you love yourself. My
stomach clenched at that thought. What does that even
mean? How do I love myself? Do I deserve to be loved?
These questions filled my brain as I put the book aside and
hugged Jeff. But enough about love, the New York City
Marathon was the next day. Let's go!

On the day of the marathon, I woke up with back stiffness.
But nothing that would stop me from toeing the line. This
is how I felt most mornings, so I got moving to loosen up. I
was glad the buses that would take me to the start line
were a half-mile away. It would feel good to walk. Once I
got to the start line, my mind shifted to all the runners
surrounding me, the music, and listening to the announcer
for when to head to the starting area. As I got going the
distraction of the crowds, cheering, and runners silenced
my discomfort. I smiled. *I made it. I'm racing again!* This
feeling of joy came over me. I felt for the first time like I did
in 2002 before all the pain commanded my attention. I
finished the New York City Marathon in a time of 3:51:21. I
was back!

Finishing the New York City Marathon was the brain
triumph I needed. It was the evidence I could build on. *My
body is strong, robust, and adaptable.* I can run marathons,
even with setbacks. Accepting the discomfort allowed me
to stay calm and keep running. *This is pain I can recognize,*

and it isn't harmful. The context of people cheering, the
music, the scenery, and Jeff waiting for me at the finish was
what helped me through the race. Running made me feel
alive, joyful, and free. It felt amazing to be racing again,
knowing that I could manage the setbacks as they came,
with Jeff by my side. I was starting to believe that the hard
work in therapy was paying off. I was on the path to
healing, and my dream of Boston was one step closer.

New York City Marathon 2011

After I ran the New York City Marathon, I was convinced
that if I kept running and continued with my talk therapy,
my pain would no longer show up. I figured running
would manage any physical discomfort and relieve work
stress. The talk therapy would continue to bring light to all
the caves I had closed off for so many years. I seemed to be
managing things well in my mind. When Jeff and I got

married a year later, I was on top of the world. My relationship with food was improving, I was running every day, and my setbacks were less frequent.

When I learned I was pregnant, I was excited but also nervous and scared. As a physical therapist, I was aware of the possible pain and discomfort pregnancy can bring. My mind started racing. *Will I be able to manage my pain if I can't run? Do I have what it takes to get through nine months of this? What about the weight gain? Ugh.* I was just starting to accept how my body was. Now it was going to change, and it worried me. I didn't want the weight gain to trigger another setback with my eating. I was glad to be in therapy still and, to my surprise, the pregnancy was a blessing. My thoughts about food changed as I was now thinking about this little human inside of me. It triggered healthy behaviors instead. I became interested in what foods to eat that would nourish our baby and me during the next nine months. My son wasn't even born, yet he was already influencing me to improve my health and be kinder to myself.

My goal changed. Training for another marathon to get into Boston became training for childbirth and improving my relationship with myself. I attempted to continue running, but my body wasn't cooperating. I opted to walk instead. I refused to beat myself up, though deep down I wanted to be that woman who ran while she was pregnant. I saw other women do it and even compete in races while pregnant. I wanted that to be me. I had to let it go, though. I wasn't that woman, and that's okay. *I will walk and strength train instead, which will get me ready to deliver our baby and be enough to keep my pain manageable.* My new training was focused on eating well, being kind to myself, going to therapy, and doing movements that felt good. The goal was to improve my overall health, as I was going to be a mom. *Yikes!* I had to get a move on. Nine months isn't a lot of time.

Jeff and Me, Sept 15 2012

Chapter Twelve
Motherhood Motivates

My tears
I had to fight
I could now face my fears
Motherhood I would need, my might
My light

Becoming a mother was not something I thought about. When I met Jeff, I was in therapy still sorting out my divorce, my pain, and unraveling all the crap that came up. I was like a honeycomb of caves. I dealt with one cave of hurt and tears, felt a moment of relief, then there was another cave I had to enter to examine and make sense of. *Will this ever end?!* I had no idea how many caves I would have to enter until I became a mom.

After my son was born, I was determined to get back to running not only to help with my pain but to help cope with my new role as a mother. My milk wasn't coming in, Brindsley wasn't gaining weight as he should, and I was blaming myself. Running has always been a way for me to manage my stress, so once the doctor cleared me, I was back to running.

When Brindsley went down for his nap, I would head down to the basement and run on the treadmill. (I didn't listen to the advice, "When the baby sleeps, you sleep.") I would turn on the music, cover the treadmill screen with my shirt, and run; I didn't want to see the time, the pace, or the mileage. I wanted to get my body back, get moving again at my pace, though my thoughts were not kind or gentle. My mind, shouting, *I should already be running an 8-minute-mile pace by now. I can't believe how slow I am!*

I was not patient with myself or my body. I was sleep-deprived, and my inner critic was easy to listen to. I started to question whether I would be able to run a marathon again. I would look at my watch and see an 11-minute-mile pace. *Ugh, I have a long way to go if I want to qualify for Boston.* I wasn't sure if I would be able to get back to that level of training. How do mothers do this? I was barely logging three miles and was out of breath and fatigued.

As I ran those several months after pregnancy, I couldn't believe that I ran a marathon before. I felt so exposed as I ran with the extra weight around my middle, around my chest, and my thoughts quickly resumed without me fighting them off: *You are disgusting. You are so slow. You can barely run three miles.* I was starting to panic that I wouldn't be able to lose the weight, I would never get past three miles, and my body wouldn't allow me to run marathons again!

Wait a second … I carried a tiny human inside of me for nine months and then gave birth without medications. If I can do that, I can run a marathon again! It was with that thought that my mind shifted. There was no questioning or resistance. I believed right away. Determined to get my running legs back and call myself a marathoner, I made a plan.

The plan was to begin training for the Rochester Half Marathon seven months away. *I can do that. I have enough time*, I reassured myself. I printed out a training plan and followed it exactly. My sister-in-law, Cindy, was going to run it too. This would keep me accountable, with no chance of backing out. She lived in Rochester, and I would be able to stay with her.

I'd wake up at 4:30 a.m. to get my training run in before heading to work. I gradually increased my mileage each week and was happy to see my eight-minute-mile pace with only two months to go. *Wow! I can do this.* My endurance was improving and running ten miles was becoming effortless. I no longer needed to walk and could finish the longer training runs easily. I continued to remind myself that running is my gift. I was made for this. That was the story I wanted to tell myself and believe. It was the mindset I wanted. During my training, I continued my therapy, worked through setbacks, and focused on healthy eating. Brindsley was my motivation to focus on my health, not just physical but mental and emotional.

Jeff stayed home with Brindsley, and I drove out to Cindy's the night before the half marathon. I was grateful to stay with her, as she would drive us to the race that morning. I felt tremendous guilt to be leaving Brindsley at only seven months old. This was my first time being away from him. *Is it okay to leave him? He's still a baby.* Jeff reassured me that everything would be fine and encouraged me to have fun. It's boys' weekend, he joked. I was grateful Jeff was supportive of my running. He is a wonderful, loving, and caring dad. Brindsley and I were truly blessed. My heart was full as I packed up the car and said my goodbyes. I cuddled Brindsley in my arms for a while, taking in that sweet baby smell. *I'll see you tomorrow, my buddy.* I gave Jeff a big hug and kiss. *Thank you. I love you.*

I was nervous as I toed the start line but excited to be back to racing. We all crowded together at the start elbow to elbow. I was grateful to be here. I was grateful for my body. It's hard to believe that just seven months ago I had Brindsley. I was proud of myself for sticking to my goal. I can be a mother and a runner. I looked at Cindy who has three children, thinking, *If she can do it, so can I.* I was happy to be here on the line with my sister-in-law. *We are mother runners.*

My goal was to run an eight-minute-mile pace for 13.1 miles. I wore my watch to keep track. I was determined to achieve my goal. I didn't want to waste any time at the hydration stops, so I carried my own hydration. When I crossed the finish line, I was bursting with pride. I did it! I finished. I could call myself a runner again. I couldn't wait to get home to show Jeff and Brindsley the medal.

***

Three months after the Rochester Half Marathon, I stared down at three pregnancy tests. I had to be certain. All three show the same thing. *I am pregnant.* Well, training for the Boston Marathon will be on hold another year. This wasn't planned. God sure does have a sense of humor. *Really God, do you think I can do this again?* He knew I could, and His plan was perfect.

We welcomed Delaney to the world in August 2014. Our world changed dramatically from one baby to two, but we embraced it. We were blessed with two healthy and happy babies. Seven months after Delaney was born, I was back on the starting line of the Syracuse Half Marathon. *I ran a half marathon seven months after Brindsley was born, I will do the same with Delaney. There will be no favoritism.*

The training was definitely trickier with two babies, yet I found a way. The treadmill and I had a love-hate relationship. On the morning of the race, I took two spoonfuls of Pepto and brought along an Imodium AD. I was not feeling well, yet I refused to stay home. *I've done this many times before, I'll be fine.* Jeff stayed home with Brindsley and Delaney, and I drove 40 minutes to Syracuse. My stomach was uneasy, yet my mind stayed positive. *I can do this. My training has been solid. Philippians 4:13. I can do all things through Christ who strengthens me.*

The weather conditions were not ideal for March, 16 degrees Fahrenheit with a wind chill of two. It was freezing. It didn't bother me. I've been training in this weather all winter. I joined the crowd of runners on the start line, thankful to be here once again. My goal was to beat my time from 2013, yet I reminded myself to enjoy the racing scene and have fun. *I promise I will not beat myself up at the finish.* The gun goes off and I look ahead at all the runners in front of me. I'm racing. My stomach settles. I have my watch on to keep track of my pace, but I don't bother to look at it. My mind wanders to Jeff and my children. I wonder what they are doing. I'm so grateful Jeff continues to support my dream and is a loving, patient dad. I smile.

At mile nine my stomach starts to rumble and my fear of having to use the bathroom occupies my mind. *Oh great, I don't see any porta-potties.* I reach in my pocket for the Imodium AD — definitely not something I would recommend — in hopes to buy me more time. I only have four miles left. *I can make it.* I'm getting to the finish line. I turn my attention to breathing, the other runners, the few people who showed up on this cold day to cheer us on, anything to keep my mind off the bathroom. I was so relieved to see the finish line. I picked up my pace, eager to rush for a toilet. I stopped my watch as I crossed the finish, grabbed my medal, and kept right on running to the bathroom. I made it. *Phew! Thank you, body. Thank you, God.*

My circumstances were not ideal, but my mind searched for the positives instead of the negatives. Positivity was a better tool. Managing my thoughts about the weather, how I was feeling, and the need for a restroom mattered in my finish today. I brought a good attitude, and my result was finishing the race at the same pace I did in 2013 despite the circumstances. Our circumstances will not always be ideal in life or in running, yet that's okay. My circumstances do not need to change to get the result I want. It's my thoughts that matter. I can decide what to think. That's what I have control over and can change.

I was starting to see the power of my thoughts; how easy it was for me to spiral into death and tragedy with just one thought. Luckily, I was noticing that I could shift to life and joy just as easily with the sentences in my mind. It was up to me, no one else, and that was all I needed to start challenging those harsh sentences that were still so easily accessible. Those sentences from childhood were untrue and outdated. *I can fight back.* Yet as a new mama with two babies, I forgot the power I had and the knowledge I had gained about pain. I was so tired and was struggling with the relationships in my family. My self-care was taking a backseat. My inner voice, my courage, became very quiet. I started to slip into my old thinking and patterns. Maybe it was the lack of sleep, the fear that I wasn't good enough for motherhood, or the pressure to choose to stay at home or return to work. Either way, I was feeling it in my physical body and in new places.

One morning after a run, my left big toe became extremely painful and red. I thought maybe it was time for a new pair of sneakers. Did you know our feet can change after pregnancy?! I had no idea. I was a half-size bigger, apparently! *Easy fix, get the right sneakers and pain will go away.* I was wrong. It did not. There were days I would have to stop running and walk. There were days I wouldn't be able to run at all.

As I played more with my children on the floor, I noticed I had intense right hip pain and stiffness. It wouldn't allow me to sit "crisscross applesauce" on the floor. When I tried to push through the pain and sit in that position, I had a hard time getting up and was limping for a few minutes, hunched over before I could resume my normal, upright walk. I thought maybe I needed to do more stretches or more strengthening. I didn't think at the time it was something I needed to get help for. My ego stepped in. *I'm a physical therapist, I can figure it out.*

The pain continued for over a year before I finally decided I had better see a rheumatologist. My concern was possible psoriatic arthritis because I did have psoriasis.

The rheumatologist was very short with me and after examination, x-rays, and blood work, he told me I had

rheumatoid arthritis and psoriatic arthritis. He then left the
room. He made no time for a supportive conversation or
questions. I was upset, confused, and scared.

What did this mean?

Does this mean I can't run? Does this mean it's going to get
worse as I get older? Will I be able to play and care for my
children? The thoughts began to spiral, and I was freaking
out.

He told me I had rheumatoid arthritis and psoriatic
arthritis. I was having multiple joint pain, psoriasis,
stiffness lasting much of the morning, and redness and
pain in my big toe. I could agree with possible psoriatic
arthritis, but not rheumatoid arthritis. He came back into
the room and told me to go to my dermatologist to get on
Humira, a very strong biologic medication with many side
effects. It isn't something to start taking without a good
deal of consideration and supportive conversation, in my
opinion — neither of which he could offer me. I left and
wanted a second opinion.

I had treated patients with both psoriatic arthritis and
rheumatoid arthritis, so I wasn't convinced this was true
for me. I went to another rheumatologist about 90 minutes
from my home. He was thorough and listened. He took x-
rays and blood work. When I told him my symptoms of
stiffness in the morning, redness, swelling, and pain in my

left big toe, low back and right hip pain, stiffness as well as mouth sores he said, "That's psoriatic arthritis."

Psoriatic arthritis was not in the plan. I was angry, confused, and frustrated. I didn't want to believe it, and deep down something was nudging me and telling me to keep searching for answers.

But I guess it did explain the multiple joint pain and stiffness, mouth sores, and fatigue. My left big toe was always so red, swollen, and painful. I was starting to look for evidence, to prove to myself that this diagnosis was my truth.

I accepted it, especially after getting a second opinion, and began researching obsessively what it all meant. It was four years of wrapping my head around autoimmune conditions. *What will my life look like in ten years? Will running still be a possibility? Does this mean medications soon or in the future? Should I let go of my goal of getting to the Boston Marathon?*

I had so many questions. There was so much uncertainty.

I went back to something my therapist repeatedly would say to me. "Julie, what can you control right now?" And saying that to myself gave me the power back.

I could control my sleep hygiene routine, staying active, learning, and talking to others, self-care, my thoughts, and my daily diet, which were exactly what I've been working on up until this diagnosis. There was a lot I had control over. There was also a lot more to learn, especially about food and the immune system.

Chapter Thirteen
Deep Breaths

Courage

Facing my fears

Daring, tenacity

Facing my challenges head-on

Be brave

My next appointment with the rheumatologist was at a different location. I gave myself plenty of time to get there in case I needed to pull over and walk around. Even though it was only 90 minutes away, I was still uneasy driving for longer than 30 minutes. It felt dangerous. I used to love road trips and driving. Now my brain thinks a road trip means pain, is not good for my back, and will make me worse.

I felt a slight ache in my low back as I set out to make the drive. *I can do this.* I turned on my favorite radio station and sang. *This will help get me there.* I reminded myself that what I think about my pain matters, and to look for my safety. *You like driving. You can sing out loud and pick the music you want. This will be fun.*

I arrived at the doctor's office, and I didn't get lost. It is a huge brain triumph for me as I walked into the office building feeling the same as when I left. *Wow! I'm hardly stiff and I didn't get any tingling or numbness in my legs when I was driving. This is awesome!* As I sat on the exam table waiting for the doctor, my body relaxed. I went over the questions in my head I wanted to ask him about. I wanted to get clarification that running is no problem even if I have psoriatic arthritis. (Several people had said I shouldn't be running, that it will make my joint pain worse). I had been researching to see if this is true and hadn't found any evidence that running isn't a good idea. I wanted to hear his thoughts on this. I also wanted to ask him about nutrition. Should I eliminate any foods from my daily diet to see if there is a change in my symptoms?

Unfortunately, I wasn't able to ask any of my questions. His nurse entered the room in a hurried fashion without introducing herself. She quickly sat on the stool and opened my chart on the computer. With her eyes glued to the screen, she asked, "What is the level of your pain today?"

Ugh, I hate this question. In the years seeing docs for my pain challenge, the question that annoyed me the most was, "What's your pain today from one to ten?" I feel like I'm in school again and don't know the right answer. I'm silent for a few seconds, my mind racing with what number is the best to say. I wonder If I said ten would they send me to the hospital? If I said one, would they believe me?

What does the number really tell them about my pain or me? It tells them nothing, and you have only ten minutes with me, so let's get to some better questions. There is no number I can give that represents what this pain means, what I'm missing out on, and what I've lost. A number doesn't tell you anything about my pain. It's a poor question and I would love to be asked better questions like, "What does this pain mean to you?" or, "What are you not doing that you would like to get back to?" or "What is your concern?" There is so much knowledge you can learn about a person with those questions. I'm not sure what you learn, if anything, from the pain rating scale.

She kept her eyes glued to the screen as she waited for my answer. "It's three today." She typed that in and proceeded with one question after the other. I felt attacked by her questioning.

The conversation went something like this:

"Have you had a 'sausage digit'?"

"What?! No."

"Have your fingers or toes ever looked like sausages?"

"No, my big toe does get swollen and red but doesn't look like a sausage."

Her face crinkled a bit and she looked back at her computer screen. Does she think I'm lying? What is she trying to say, that I don't have psoriatic arthritis?

"Oh, you're a chronic runner."

I got super defensive and confused at that statement. Chronic runner? So what is she saying, this pain is my fault? I felt my pain increase at that moment. My chest tightened to fight back the tears and my body tensed up. My back stiffness that had been a three became an eight, and it was telling me to run. LEAVE NOW. I couldn't. I was glued to the table, my breathing shallow as I looked down at my sneakers. I didn't feel good. I didn't feel safe. I started crying when she left.

When the nurse came back in with the doctor, he asked, "What's wrong?"

I couldn't answer for fear I wouldn't be able to control my emotions. I just shook my head. My disappointment in myself grew as I kept my mouth shut. Once again, I don't have a voice. I was mad at myself for not leaving or at least getting clarification by what she meant with her statements. I cowered instead and went through with the examination like a good patient as I fought back the tears. He grabbed my leg to test my hip joint and I tensed up, holding my breath. I just wanted to be done with it.

At the end of the appointment, he felt I needed more testing, a full body bone scan, and more blood work. Whether this decision was made based on the examination or me crying uncontrollably because of the pain, I will not know. Looking back, it was probably my emotional outburst that led him in that direction, and I've had to forgive myself for that. If I had been able to keep my composure and explain calmly why my pain increased in that office, I may have saved myself from the humiliation, unanswered questions, and future appointments. I learned a lot that day. My pain went from mild stiffness to extreme stiffness by sitting in that office, and I know why. There was more danger than safety, and the great protector was there to let me know. I am not crazy!

The protectometer is right. The danger messages were what I was hearing (you're a chronic runner, you haven't had a sausage digit), what I was seeing (questionable glares, no eye contact or warm demeanor), the lack of interaction with the nurse (staring at her computer), what I was making her words mean (this pain is my fault), the things I was saying to myself (does she not believe me, I hate when they ask me to rate my pain), and not asking the questions I had planned. I didn't feel safe in that office, and my nervous system, which watches out for me and is my alarm system, turned the volume up. I wasn't in real danger, but my central nervous system had more evidence of danger than safety, so my pain increased. I took some deep breaths. *Okay, I'm on to something.*

I continued my care, seeing him when needed, but I felt this new confidence in myself having the protectometer. I could confidently say, "I know what to do," because of what happened at that last appointment. For the first time, I believed that pain was possible when there was more evidence of danger than safety. I experienced it firsthand. I continued to learn about autoimmune conditions. I started to dive into more of the nutrition side. Could it be something I'm eating that's contributing? I wasn't sure, so I needed to do more research and stay curious.

In the meantime, I would keep running and not let this diagnosis deter me from my dream.

Chapter Fourteen
My Light

My light
God is with me
Leading me down the path
Motherhood gave me the courage
Glowing

My next race was on the calendar, and my goal over the
next few months was to work on speed. I was excited to get
back into the racing scene more consistently. It was a crisp,
cool morning as I parked my car in the field next to the
racing tents. I was at the Lafayette Apple Run, an 18K race,
and it was great to see other runners I knew. My nerves
relaxed a bit and I felt more at home. As I warmed up for
the race, I reminded myself to have fun but to push myself,
see what I can do. The last few months I'd felt great with
minimal setbacks, and though the recent diagnosis of
psoriatic arthritis lingered in my mind, I wasn't going to let
it take up space or stop me from running. I was made to
run.

As I walked toward the start line, I looked around me,
soaking in the beauty of the trees in yellow, orange, and
red, the sun just peeking behind the clouds. I heard the
conversations of the other runners. As I toed the line, I felt

strong and relaxed. I was going to have a great race; I'd already made up my mind. The gun went off and I raced to the front, keeping my eye on the other women runners. I was determined to stay as close to them as I could.

At mile three an intense, stingy, sharp pain shot at the outside of my left knee. *Oh no, I'm not stopping, I'm only three miles in and don't know the course.* I didn't want to lose the pack of runners, I needed to stay with them. *Find a way, Julie.* My mind stayed calm. *Okay, this is just your nerves talking. You can do this; you've had this pain before.* I shifted my posture and the pain moved to my back. *Hmm, that's weird. Okay, I can deal with the pain in my back as long as I can keep it out of my leg.* I found that if I shortened my stride and ran more upright, the pain stayed in my back and my leg felt great. *Awesome, I can keep running,* I thought as another female runner came up beside me. I wasn't going to let her go so I ran with her.

My mind replayed the thought, *Stay with her, and keep your stride short and quick.* We ran together for the next six miles and my mind was so focused on keeping with her cadence that the pain was minimal. If I felt it in my leg, I was able to find the sweet spot to turn it off. My confidence grew. I was in charge. My mind stayed calm and positive. *I can stay with her. Don't back down, I can keep this pace.*

We both passed a few more runners and, with a mile to go, she started to fade behind me. Once I saw the finish, I kicked it in and crossed the line. I felt great after the race. I didn't have any pain in my leg or back. Pain is so weird, but I didn't have time to think much more about it as Jeff and the kids rushed over to me with congratulatory hugs.

When I got home, I thought about the race. How did I manage to keep going, run at a great pace, and ignore the pain? My mind was calm, positive, and strong. I didn't freak out or panic. I believed the pain wasn't dangerous and that I was in charge. I was able to find a way to keep running and focus on my goal of staying with the lead runners. I didn't entertain any negative thoughts. I talked myself into it and my body listened. I was beginning to understand the power of my mind and how it mattered when it came to my pain.

The next day, the pain returned. I felt the stinging sharp pain in my back, and it traveled down to the outside of my left knee. I was so frustrated. *Why is this pain showing up now? Please, don't last long, I'm just getting back to racing*, I pleaded. I was limping when I walked, and I couldn't run. I began to panic, and the movements that in the past would take the pain away or lessen it were not working. As I was doing the movements, I was agitated with my body. *I just ran a great race, so why is this happening to me? Why did I wake up with this pain when I went to bed feeling great?* I continued to ask why, and the answer was that I didn't know; it only caused me to feel more disempowered. It was a real dream stealer.

I didn't understand my pain like I thought I did, and I was becoming more frustrated and angrier. I thought this nerve pain was over with. *I've been in therapy for seven years now, I'm back to running, I thought I was done with this. I've been doing really hard work, confronting my past and I'm still in therapy.* But now a new thought came into my mind: *Is this pain psoriatic arthritis? Do I need medication?* I wanted answers and went back to my books, researching and learning to understand more. I remembered back to a course I took on the nervous system and my instructor said that oftentimes an autoimmune condition causes increased sensitivity of the nervous system. *Is this what's going on with me? A sensitive nervous system?* The more I read through my notes and *Explain Pain* textbook, the more I understood the importance of the nervous system and the immune system. They are connected. The neuroimmune system is what they called it. I need to focus on getting my nervous system healthier.

The burning and sharp pain at the outside of my left knee would move to my right knee. That was odd. The fact that I could run and make it go away confirmed to me that this wasn't a muscle or tissue injury. The pain wouldn't go away. The stiffness in my back and tingling and numbness in my feet was increasing my curiosity. *Are all these symptoms related to the increased sensitivity of my nervous system?* The more I researched about autoimmune conditions the more I learned that the answer to that question was *Yes*. I shifted my focus away from the herniated disc, sacroiliac joint, iliotibial band, and my knee. *This isn't about my structure. This is about my neuroimmune system.* I was still uncertain about the psoriatic arthritis diagnosis, but my psoriasis was visible on my elbow, knees, scalp, feet, and pubic area as red, itchy, bleeding at times, and painful. I was determined to understand my body better and so I immersed myself in further readings, research articles, and courses about pain.

***

After Brindsley was born, I started having nightmares. I would wake up with tears some nights because the dreams were so real. They were from the past. These were the dreams that you remember the next day. They were traumatic, painful things that I never spoke about, not even in therapy. I hadn't thought I needed to, but to be honest, I was afraid. I was afraid to bring up these secrets. *What would she think of me? Would she still want to work with me? Is there something wrong with me?*

As I began uncovering my dangers (DIM) in the seven categories, my body was not happy. There were some big DIMs, ones I never told anyone about. This tool was great for me because it forced me to write it out, which then gave me the courage to speak it. I was able to share with my therapist my eating disorder, the pills, the suicidal thoughts, and she stuck with me! I'm forever grateful I had her come alongside me during this really painful time. It's not something I could've done alone.

Motherhood motivated me to face the past, the dark secrets I was carrying, and gave me the courage to speak my truth. I was determined to not let my burdens become my children's. I didn't know at the time that these caves from my earlier years were contributing to my pain experience and that entering them, looking around, and even loving them would be a factor in my pain recovery.

Four months after Brindsley was born I started to feel this tingling sting on the right side of my torso that wrapped around the right side of my back. When I lifted my shirt, I saw a red rash covering that part of my body and it was itchy. *What is this? It's a crazy, red, bumpy rash. Is this poison ivy?* I was a new mom — how I thought it was poison ivy makes me laugh now. I wasn't hiking or enjoying the woods, I was navigating a full-time job, a shift in family dynamics, diaper changes, bottle feedings, and lack of sleep. I was not outside in the woods or gardening!

The conflicts arising between my in-laws, parents, and husband combined with the expectations I was placing on myself as a new mother were nerve-racking. This pain and skin rash was the result. My body was burning at me.

I ignored the pain for two weeks until the stingy, zapping, itching was unbearable. I couldn't think straight. The pain was waking me up at night. When I lifted my shirt up to show the doctor, she immediately declared, "Oh my gosh, you have shingles."

"Shingles?! Are you sure?"

"Oh yes, this is shingles."

I was shocked, shingles isn't something I thought a 33-year-old gets, but apparently, age doesn't matter.

She was concerned and encouraged me to take a few days off from work to get some rest. She handed me a white square piece of paper. "Go get this filled." There was urgency in her voice. "This medication will help the nerve pain."

I took her advice. I was so tired.

Being a new mom was more of a challenge than I expected. The struggle to work or not work, the opinions and advice you don't ask for, and the dreaded, "Oh, you aren't breastfeeding, you really should be breastfeeding, that's the best for your baby." That comment made me cower with shame and guilt. I felt like I was under a microscope with every move being scrutinized and judged. The pressure to please and be perfect was exposing itself once again, rumination consuming my mind. *Why did I let that happen? Why didn't I say something? Why did I say yes, again?* It was exhausting, my old thought patterns and habits revealing that there was work to be done and my therapist acknowledging that I may need more than she could offer. She recommended eye movement desensitization and reprocessing (EMDR) and gave me the psychologist's name and number. It was time to link up with another clinician to help me with the next steps to healing.

My nervous system was reliving the past not only in the daytime with my rumination but also in my dreams, which were more like nightmares. My therapist explained that eye movement desensitization and reprocessing was a therapy to heal my mind from the psychological trauma and to help me change my story from, "I'm in danger, I'm going to die," to, "It's over, I'm safe now," without a physical response. I could feel my physical response during this time, manifesting as knots in my stomach, tightness, stiffness in my low back, my chest tightening, tingling, and numbness in my legs and feet. I was having a huge pain response working through this type of therapy. My nervous system was on high alert, looking out for me because these memories were linked to danger. *You are not safe.* Even though I was sitting safely on a couch in my therapist's office and in no physical danger, my brain was getting it wrong. Those pain memories were linked to this physical response I was having, even though it wasn't needed now. I didn't need protection, but my nervous system and brain thought I did. It was doing what it learned. It was trying to protect me. It was being that overprotective parent and that's what I wanted to change because it wasn't serving me anymore. This desensitization therapy was a tool to help my brain heal. Now, when I think of moments from my childhood, I no longer feel pain. I feel compassion.

This therapy treatment was a way for me to access and process my traumatic memories, as well as a way to resolve them and heal. It was hard and painful, not only emotionally but physically. I kept pushing courage through this time and I could start to see a shift. The nightmares were letting up and so was my pain. I felt a huge sense of relief to bring what I was carrying out to the light. Motherhood was my light. It was shining on all those dark caves I didn't want to enter and giving me the courage to face them head-on. I was going to keep showing up to therapy, coaching, and running for not only myself but my family. *I will figure out why this pain is persisting, and I will not give up.*

Chapter Fifteen
My Language was a Pain Trigger

My pain
Words were a key
It wasn't just the shame
It took me a while to see
I'm free

"My back is killing me!" Do you ever say this?

I used to say this a lot. It's a common metaphor that many say when they hurt. It's not actually killing us, but we are sure making it worse with our language.

Saying that over and over was indeed a threat to me and my nervous system, so it makes sense that the great protector would step in. I learned to replace my words with something more helpful or safe to improve my pain challenge.

When I have a setback now, I catch myself. It has been a habit for me to immediately say this but now I have other choices, such as: "I am sore but safe," "My back is out of sync with the rest of my body," or "My hip is not as loose as I would like it."

This was an "aha!" moment for me and why this one memory from childhood was so important to work through in desensitization therapy. It was summertime, I was driving the tractor in the field in charge of raking the hay that day. My dad briefly explained how he wanted the rows of hay raked, how to operate the rake, and a quick review of driving the tractor. It was something I had a hard time remembering. I didn't do it every day and wasn't confident at all. I already felt my stomach knotting up as I began to rake, keeping vigilant and making sure I did the rows perfectly. *I can't mess up. Julie, you have to remember what he said about how he wants the rows.*

One section of the field had a small hill, as I drove up, I didn't give the tractor enough gas and the tractor rolled backward right over the brand-new rake! I freaked out. This was a brand-new rake. *My dad is going to kill me!* I couldn't stop repeating that in my head. I started to shake and cry hysterically as my stomach knotted up, my chest tightened, and my heart raced. Fear was hard to handle, it paralyzed me. *What should I do?!*

I rushed to a house nearby to call my mom for help and thankfully she picked up the phone and came and got me.

I get in the back of the van and curl up in a ball on the floor. The maroon carpet is all I can see through my tears. The thought, 'Dad is going to kill me,' plays over and over in my mind. I can't stop crying and I just want to die. I don't want to face my dad. What will he say or do? My mom doesn't say a word and drives to a farmer's friend to have him pick up the tractor and bring it back to our farm. I'm praying mom will just take me home, so I don't have to face dad, but instead, she drops me off at the barn and leaves me there with him. My dad is furious, judging by the turn of his hat and red face, he has already seen the rake and he is pissed. I couldn't speak, all I could do was stand there, hostage to the yells of, 'You're so stupid,' 'What is wrong with you, don't you know how to drive?' and 'That's a brand-new rake!'

I was in tenth grade when this happened, and it was one of the memories I needed to sort out in desensitization therapy. I had no idea how much that affected me, it was so long ago but after having my first child this memory is what resurfaced. I shoved it down and didn't want to talk about it, but I was now making the connection of how my language and pain were linked. I understand now why saying "my back is killing me" was such a threat. That memory contributed to my pain experience and my language was the trigger.

***

Are there some unhelpful metaphors that may need rethinking? I used to say, "My back is out, again!" Seriously, I would get so frustrated. I would have intense pain in my low back and wasn't able to bend over. My muscles would seize up, so moving freely was very difficult. I didn't realize how unhelpful this statement was.

I knew my back wasn't out, where would it go???... but even so, I would say this.

I didn't think what I said had anything to do with my pain experience. Like what I say doesn't matter. I was wrong. It certainly does and there is research and evidence to now prove this. I was starting to make the connection. What I say and believe about myself matters, my mind matters. I discovered it was a contributor to my pain. I can manage my mind in everyday life just like when I run and the side effect — which I wasn't even aware of yet — was less pain!

This language is threatening and not helpful. Our body parts can't "go out" unless we have a dislocation. Your body can't "go out" or you can't "throw something out." It's a common language though, isn't it? Just like when I hear "I have a pinched nerve." These are not healthy metaphors and I think it's important we rethink the language we say to ourselves and others.

This was not easy for me. It was such a habit. I catch myself now when I am about to say it to myself after a setback occurs. I now say, "My back is out of sync today."

I realized that rethinking my language was important to my recovery. It mattered. I was able to unlearn this limiting belief that my back was fragile. A better explanation for me was that it's more likely that my joints are a little inflamed, sticky, or irritated, but never "out."

I now believe that my spine is supported by SUPER strong ligaments and muscles, things aren't going anywhere. My body is strong, robust, and adaptable. Our language is important, and this was another thing I wanted to consider on my pain recovery journey. Just being aware of what we say is a good start to improving our health.

Chapter Sixteen
Rethinking Pain

Pain can change, I've learned
Sensitivity not fixed
I'm bioplastic

When I began researching pain and pain neuroscience, I couldn't believe what I was reading. Wait. What?! Pain is produced in the brain, not in the body? I had to stop reading, my brain hurt. It was challenging everything I believed and how I practiced as a physical therapist.

The thoughts rushed in. So, is this my fault? Why didn't anyone tell me this before? Can I change my brain? I've been treating my patients all wrong.

These thoughts filled my days, but I kept reading. I was determined to get up to date not only for me but for my patients. I stayed curious. I was committed to understanding what the research and other clinicians were finding. I wanted to accept the mind-body connection. I wanted to recognize my pain so I could help others.

I continued researching the work of Lorimer Moseley and David Butler as well as Adriaan Louw, Gregory Liberman, Christopher Johnson, and Peter O'Sullivan. They opened my eyes to a wealth of information and knowledge. It got my attention. I began to question my beliefs about pain and what I was taught. They gave me a new focus, purpose, and hope. They were different. They were interested in guiding patients on their pain recovery journey.

One thing that stood out was bioplasticity, which is the idea that everything in our body, including our nervous system, changes and adapts. We are adaptable, bioplastic learners until our last breath. How amazing. Of course, there is a healthy side to bioplasticity and an unhealthy side.

My tissues and joints hurt, but the problem lies in my nervous system. My pain was real, but I couldn't recall any injury to explain it. Running was always to blame. The simple response was, "You need to stop running." I listened, thinking that my pain would go away, but it didn't. My shame, anger, negative self-talk, lack of knowledge, avoidance of certain movements and activities, caused my body to adapt in an unhealthy way.

This is the side of bioplasticity working against me. I lost muscle because I wasn't lifting anything. I gained weight. I was eating unhealthy food to numb my pain. I wasn't exercising, which made my depression worse and affected my sleep. My body was adapting to the demands I was placing on it, which were no demands. By not moving, strengthening, managing my mind, or eating the right foods for me, every single system in my body was adapting in a damaging way for my health.

Luckily because of bioplasticity I could go the other direction and regain my health. This was the hope I needed. I can undo these maladaptive changes. I can retrain my pain system to be less protective. I have bioplasticity on my side and I believe in this. I am bioplastic. My pain is not fixed, it is always changing. When I thought about this knowledge, I knew it was true. Some moments I would have intense pain and other times I wouldn't. It was never the same intensity all day long. My new thought was, *This current level of sensitivity is not fixed. I am bioplastic.*

I continued reading, researching, and listening to podcasts to gain more knowledge. I reminded myself repeatedly, *This current level of sensitivity is not fixed, I am bioplastic.* Saying this during a setback was a way for me to not freak out. I wrote this on a piece of paper so I could see it throughout the day. I placed it on my computer screen, in my car, and bathroom mirror. I wanted this to be my go-to thought loop. I needed to see it more every day. I wanted this constant reminder that my pain is not fixed, it can change. This thought was helping me retrain my brain.

I was starting to believe the idea that pain and the brain are highly connected. *When I experience more safety than danger, my pain decreases.* I stayed curious and experimented with the question: *What are the things in my life that make me feel safe, happy, and calm?* I was starting to understand that if my brain doesn't think I need protection then my pain will decrease.

I needed to seek out my SIMs to re-conceptualize my pain. I wanted to shift from, "This pain is dangerous," to, "This is protecting me." *If I can give my body and brain evidence of safety throughout my day, I can teach my system to be less protective. This will change my pain experience.* I wanted to give my body evidence of safety and to do this I needed to be what the Protectometer Handbook refers to as a SIM-seeker!

Each day I would write down three to five things that make me feel calm and happy. I would then take action by implementing them in my day. It's become a daily practice and one tool I use to bring me pain relief. The one category I focused on most was, "The things I say to myself." My thoughts were like a virus and a danger I needed to confront.

One thing I have learned is to never underestimate the power of the human body-mind connection! There is <u>no</u> separation. What we *think* affects our body and what we *do* affects our mind.

So, I got to writing those SIMS down each day and began adding them back into my life again. I was changing my pain, little by little.

***

I can't begin to count how many people close to me and strangers would say running isn't good for your knees: "You shouldn't run so much. Running isn't good for your joints." What about all the farm work I did growing up? Lifting hay bales, picking up and carrying huge rocks from the fields, shoveling manure, and cleaning out stalls. What about all of that? How could running be bad for me compared to all this other work I had done? I would internalize the words just like all the other ones that said I was slow, fat, and stupid. Luckily, I kept running, but the words stuck in my body and mind.

When my pain was at its worst, I believed I was weak and fragile, and that I needed to be careful. I avoided certain movements, activities, and lifting. Those words from the past had become my truth. I forgot about the hard work I had endured on the farm, the tough workouts, and the distances I logged running. Instead, I believed my body was falling apart. I had evidence from the past that my body was strong and capable, but I was in so much pain that I couldn't get out of my own way.

"It's because you run." That was the dialogue I heard many times during my pain experience. Running was to blame. That's why the outside of my knee hurts. That's why my toe hurts. That's why my back and hip hurt. I wondered, if I wasn't a runner then what would they say? Would the diagnosis still be the same? It was so quickly given without much thought or examination. This was my experience. I didn't question my pain for a long time and believed it was because of running. It wasn't until I stopped running when I learned the truth. The truth for me was the pain wasn't because of running. It wasn't about tissue damage anymore — and if it was, the tissues would have healed by now.

What I know now and what the evidence tells us currently is that running is the best thing for my body. It is strengthening my bones, making my back stronger, my heart healthier, reducing my stress, and improving my mental health. The best part is that it's changing my brain. I'm building new brain cells every day. We were born to move, but when we hear these untrue messages, misconceptions of our body, and pain, I can see why we stop moving or are afraid even to try.

***

When I learned that pain is multi-dimensional and my memories of pain depend on context, my focus changed.

I recalled childbirth. Why during childbirth did I have such excruciating pain that immediately went away when I held my sweet baby boy? The context, my surroundings, beliefs, feelings, safety is how I make sense of this pain quickly softening. I was full of joy, happiness, and pride. My husband was with me. I had excellent nurses, and my doctor, who had treated me during my entire pregnancy, was there. I felt safe and cared for. I was able to have a natural childbirth, as I had prayed for. I even put myself through it again and had a beautiful baby girl 18 months later. How did I forget that pain of labor and delivery? For me, this painful memory was accompanied by joy, amazement, and a miracle. That's what I remembered, and the pain was forgotten.

Many pain scientists, Louis Gifford, Lorimer Moseley, Mick Thacker, and Pat Wall believe that our memories of pain are influenced by the meaning of that pain. What are we making our pain mean? As a marathon runner, I experience pain running over 20 miles, but that pain doesn't necessarily mean damage or that I need to stop. I expect to have pain and to be uncomfortable. What's the context here? It's my past experiences, my memories, my thoughts, and the opportunity to achieve my goal of finishing. It's my surroundings, the other runners, and the cheering crowds. When I finish the race, limping and exhausted, I'm distracted from the pain by congratulatory hugs, feelings of joy and accomplishment, and a medal hanging from my neck. Later that same day, I'm always looking for the next race I can enter.

The true question is this: What are we making our pain mean?

There was a time I was making my pain mean that I couldn't bend, do yoga, lift heavy things, or slouch. If I bent over, I felt a sharp pain. If I sat for too long, my back would tense and stiffen. When I went for a run, I would feel buzzing and tingling in my legs. Pain was that overprotective parent again, stopping me from exploring or playing with movement. *I'm as flexible as well-cooked spaghetti.* I laugh and smile when I say that. I need to repeat that sentence more. It's better than, *Ugh, I'm stiff as a board.* I would repeat this to myself as I reached down toward my toes. Actually I was lucky to get to my shins. *There was a time I could place my palms right on the floor! All the years of dancing ballet made me quite flexible. This is ridiculous!* I knew what my body was capable of, yet here we are struggling to reach my toes. *How did this happen?* I'll tell you. It was me believing that bending over was bad for my back, and that bending over would cause my disc to herniate again. *Is it really that easy?* I believed so. I'm embarrassed to admit it, yet this is what my pain experience would do to me. I couldn't think straight or question those thought viruses. I avoided bending, yoga, and slouching in a chair or couch. *No wonder why I can't touch my toes!* I'd stopped doing it. I avoided that motion, a motion my spine would benefit from to stay healthy. Just like bending backward, twisting, rotating, these movements lubricate my spine, nourish my brain, enhance oxygenation, keep my nerves sliding and gliding — the benefits go on.

These movements and activities were linked to pain because I believed that they were bad for my back. I thought it was a danger and that I was doing myself harm. This belief was linked to my pain experience and until I confronted my beliefs, bending would continually be a trigger for me. My thoughts and what I believed created this pain memory. My system was learning to protect me based on this belief alone. It was not serving me.

I wanted to change this belief. *How can I unlink pain with bending?* I learned to trick my nervous system. *What other ways can I bend my spine that doesn't hurt?* This was my experiment. I started to explore different movements to figure it out.

I wasn't able to bend over and touch my toes; it hurt too much. My back would tighten right up like someone was squeezing me. So, I found that the child's pose was a great place to start. My spine was bending, and I was face down, which allowed me to relax and close my eyes. This was a position where I could focus on my breath, practice my positive affirmations, and have minimal pain. I felt safe.

I couldn't believe it. This had been a position I've been avoiding, but I felt my body telling me to give it a go. I was starting to listen to trust my body and mind. I was exploring movements and positions that felt good. I was gaining evidence that my body is adaptable, robust, and strong. I built on this to eventually be able to bend over while standing with no problem, as well as return to yoga. I enjoy yoga now two times a week. It has helped me learn to be still, breathe better, and explore new movements. Yoga and running provides a great balance for me.

Learning and believing that my pain was about sensitivity, not damage, gave me confidence and reassurance. It changed my focus. *What else can I do to improve the health of my nervous system?* I discovered neurodynamics. This is a general term used for the health and movement of the nerves in the body. I discovered my nerves weren't injured, but they were not happy or healthy. They were irritated and extra sensitive due to my avoidance of certain movements and positions over the years. This created tightness in my hips, back, and legs, which affected the health of my nerves that take care of these body parts. Nerves want blood flow, movement, and space. I was not giving them what they wanted and that contributed to my pain. The tightness was not muscular; it was due to my nerves not being able to glide and slide through my tissue as I moved. Neurodynamic exercises are movements combining both the spine and limb (either arm or leg, or both) to decrease nerve sensitivity and restore limb movement. I found specific combinations of neurodynamic exercises that allowed me to move more and decrease the tingling, numbness, and stinging in my legs. It was also improving my spine mobility. I was giving my body evidence of safety. These movements didn't hurt, and I was slowly gaining confidence in my body, which allowed me to change my thinking. I was becoming calmer and more self-aware.

I was exploring new movements and staying curious. I focused on my breathing and poked a little more into the pain. I was retraining my system to be less reactive, and neurodynamics were movements I could do to help myself. I had another tool to add to my action plan for relief.

I repeat, *I'm as flexible as well-cooked spaghetti.* I smirk and feel this laughter inside of me. That sentence was funny, so I decided to keep saying that instead. Why not?! It creates an image of me loose, relaxed, all through my legs, arms, and spine. I'm like a rag doll flopped right over with no care in the world.

I was determined to get my movement back. I was able to touch my toes before and I will be able to touch them again. I am bioplastic. Thoughts are the superpower we all have. If I keep practicing bending over and doing other movements I've been avoiding, I will restore my motion. My thoughts as I move: I'm lubricating my joints, waking up my brain cells, and giving my nerves blood flow, movement and space. Yippee! We are made to move.

The more I learned about the neuroscience of pain, the more confident I became. Knowledge is therapy, and I was understanding more about why my pain persisted. It wasn't about re-injury during these setbacks, it was about the health of my nervous system. *What are the things that are contributing to my sensitivity?* Remember, everyone's pain experience is unique to them; however, if your pain has persisted longer than six months, this may be a great question to ask yourself.

When looking at my DIMs and SIMs, I was better able to identify what those contributors were for me. I recognized movements I was avoiding and understood that the pain was not telling me I was doing something wrong. It was telling me the nerves that take care of my legs, hip, and back are sensitive. They haven't been loved. They were sticky, irritated, and unhealthy because of my beliefs and thoughts. Once I confronted my dangers, trusted my body, and poked into my discomfort my sensitivity changed. My movements and activities grew, and so did my world.

I found that during running, if I felt the sensations in my legs or hip, this approach helped me handle them better. *My nerves are just talking to my brain, I'm okay. I'll keep running and see what happens.* Most of the time I would keep running, and the sensation would go away. Other times it would just stay the same. I was okay feeling that sensation and I stayed calm. I could run *and* have that sensation. I understood that I was not hurting myself. This was a huge brain triumph! This is what I want for you, reader. If I can do it, so can you.

Rethinking was part of my journey to recovery. It was like a breath of fresh air. It filled my lungs with curiosity, compassion, and permission to let the old ideas and beliefs go. I had a choice to make. Either I could keep digging my heels into what I knew and keep trucking along, or I could let go of everything and think again.

I chose the latter path, and it was bumpy and not well-traveled. I could understand why I kept trucking along for so much of my life; this new path was going against the status quo. It wasn't common. It was sometimes dark and lonely, and it required curiosity, courage, persistence, and patience. There was a lot of stopping along the path to set things down that I no longer needed, knowing I could come back for them or not. I was permitting myself to let go of the rules of the perfect way to sit, run, lift, or move. I found there is no perfect way. I was giving myself permission to let go of the expectations of others and to release the pressure I was putting on myself to achieve and accomplish things in order to be seen and loved.

Chapter Seventeen
To Love and Be Loved

Loyalty and laughter
One and only
Valiant
Enjoyment

My belief that my pain will get better stayed with me as I practiced what I was learning. The more I worked on myself, dug deep into the parts of me that I was hiding and ignoring, the stronger my belief grew. I did not doubt that I would run in Boston and working toward this big goal helped me achieve the small goals I was setting for myself. These were goals to start working on my relationship with food and myself and set down the belief that I couldn't love just one or the other. I can love food. It will fuel my body to heal, run, and celebrate with friends and family. And I can also love myself to heal, to forgive, and to model that for my children.

To love and be loved is what I'm just learning now in my forties. I believe this was the biggest part of my healing. My husband and children showed me this. They loved me even during all the pain setbacks, the messy bits, and they gave me a new purpose. This allowed me to start learning how to love myself and push for my dream.

My amazing family

At the kitchen table, I heard my daughter Delaney say, "I love you, mama, and I love myself." I realized at that moment I had not said that to myself. I would say the opposite: "I hate myself" or "I hate my body." That was the challenge for my mind-body connection since childhood. Every cell in my body was hearing that over and over. The belief that I'm not worthy, I'm not lovable, and there is something wrong with me had manifested. My body was surrendering without question. The biochemistry of belief was a contributor to my pain experience.

The Indian Journal of Psychiatry, 2009 Oct-Dec; 51(4): 239–241., defines the biochemistry of belief as follows: "The biochemistry of our body stems from our awareness. Belief-reinforced awareness becomes our biochemistry. Each and every tiny cell in our body is perfectly and absolutely aware of our thoughts, feelings, and of course, our beliefs. There is a beautiful saying, 'Nobody grows old. When people stop growing, they become old.' If you believe you are fragile, the biochemistry of your body unquestionably obeys and manifests it. If you believe you are tough (irrespective of your weight and bone density!), your body undeniably mirrors it. When you believe you are depressed (more precisely, when you become consciously aware of your 'Being depressed'), you stamp the raw data received through your sense organs, with a judgment – that is your personal view – and physically become the 'interpretation' as you internalize it."

Not only could I choose what to think, but I had the power to choose what to believe. I don't need to live my life now based on the information I received from my childhood. It is outdated and not true. This was empowering and exciting to learn. I started challenging my beliefs and having this knowledge made it easier for me. I smile wide and my heart grows big every time I hear Delaney say those words, "I love myself." I pray she will never forget that. She will know to love and be loved. I'm now able to say that to myself. It still feels weird to me but I'm practicing and it's getting easier. I'm changing that belief. It is part of my healing.

***

Some beliefs from childhood served me well and provided me the way through my pain journey. One belief was that if I was patient, good things would happen, good things would come. A memory that possibly brought this belief into existence was during the holidays when I was a child.

The farm chores had to come first even before opening Christmas gifts or hunting for Easter eggs. I didn't know it then, but delayed gratification was a skill the farm was teaching me. I was training my brain to wait, and this would be helpful in my pain recovery. I would wake up at 4 a.m., eager to open gifts or find Easter eggs, but the barn chores came first. I would stare at the presents, looking for mine. I wanted to open them, but I had to wait. I peeked inside my stocking. A few chocolates in red and green foil shined through the Christmas lights on the tree.

Feelings of excitement and relief mixed with impatience would overwhelm me. I would quickly get dressed for barn chores. We all rushed over to the barn, my brother and sisters and I, to get the chores done as fast as we could. It would be at least three more hours before we would get home to open gifts. We worked hard, anticipating what we would get under the tree. The reward for our work was worth the wait — presents and chocolates. We were grateful for the new gifts, as we didn't get many throughout the year.

This feeling of envy sometimes would creep in as my friends would talk about their Christmas or Easter mornings. It wasn't chores, then gifts. It was sleeping in, then opening gifts. I wanted that too. I didn't want to wait, but learning this skill helped me later. Patience was required during my road to healing, and I was happy that the ability to wait was already instilled in me. I believed deep down that my pain would get better. I needed to trust the process that my dream of getting to the Boston Marathon would come true.

***

I wasn't scared to do the work needed for my healing. The hardest part for me was to keep pushing courage during the waiting, during the setbacks. To believe that even on the bad days I'm not regressing. I'm making progress and this is what it will look like. The ups and downs are part of the journey and to not beat myself up. There is nothing that's gone wrong here. *Julie, keep climbing the mountain. Set down what you don't need, get to the top, then climb again. You will get there. The Lord is with you.*

Chapter Eighteen
Be Still

Be still

Sit in quiet

When your mind wanders, pause

Keep focusing on your breathing

Eyes closed

I'm a doer. Tell me what to do and I will do it at 110%. I'm not a person who likes to sit still and growing up on a farm may have had something to do with that. There was no time for sitting around. There was always work to do. This belief that I'm lazy if I'm not working or I'm not worthy if I'm not accomplishing something was ingrained in me. When I was reading about meditation and mindfulness, I told myself it wasn't for me. *I don't need that; I can't just sit there and do nothing.* I ignored what the research and evidence were saying about focusing on your breath or that being still was the way to strengthen your mind. I figured I had better things to do with my time, better things to help my pain than sit still.

I didn't want to believe meditation or mindfulness was for me. I resisted it for a while. I had my routine in the morning: movement, gratitude practice, thought download, and reading my daily devotions. These were all very helpful in my recovery, but they were all doing, writing, reading, or moving. I couldn't be still. I didn't know how. This was the hardest thing for me to learn, how to BE STILL. Even when I would pray, I was driving, or running, or washing dishes. I wasn't sitting still talking to God. I was always doing something. I didn't want to be lazy, and this belief that I'm not worthy unless I'm accomplishing something weighed on me.

I continued researching and learning the benefits of mindfulness and meditation, how it improves your breathing, helps you gain brain power (no more monkey mind), is a pain softener, balances emotional and mental health, and calms the nerves. I wanted all of this, but more importantly, I wanted to be able to teach my children, and that was my motivation, that's why I finally gave it a go.

I wanted to decrease my sympathetic system that had been ramped up for so many years and improve my parasympathetic system. Mindfulness meditation would allow this to happen to me. I was starting to believe that if I could stick with this daily practice, I would gain all of these wonderful benefits. This would help all areas of my life.

I downloaded an app on my phone with a variety of guided meditations to choose from. I picked a five-minute one. I could sit still for five minutes and close my eyes. The voice that I heard was calm and soothing. I felt my shoulders relax and my back release its tight grip, and I focused on my breath as she instructed. I breathed deeply in through my nose, expanding my diaphragm, and breathed out through my mouth. My mind wandered to what I needed to do or what I should be doing instead of this, but I went back to my breath. *Julie, focus on your breath.*

Those first five minutes seemed to last two hours, but the more I came back to this practice each day the easier it became. I was able to sit longer. Ten minutes then became 15 minutes, and my mind wandered less and less. I didn't feel different or better right away, but this wasn't about immediate relief, this was a practice for the long haul. I reminded myself of that. I was going to allow my body to adapt to this new practice. This would take time and patience.

I'm learning how to hold space for myself and for my children, to sit with them in their sadness or pain. To not force them to hurry up and get over it, stop crying or shove it down. As I'm learning how to be still, and I'm teaching my children, too. Let's sit with it and don't try to push it away. "I'm here to be with you," I say, and my body relaxes more, and I notice theirs does too.

This was not easy. It did not come naturally, especially because I was someone who didn't want to feel her feelings and sit with them. I would run, hide, work, or eat to numb them. Luckily, I had lots of time to practice this work — thank you, Brindsley and Delaney. Motherhood was stretching me at just the right time. If you're a mom, you know that big emotions are an everyday occurrence.

I'm learning alongside my children. This is my joy in motherhood, my start-over. I can start over. I don't have to hang on to that old story, it doesn't have to become me now. I don't need to hide from my children. I am human and pain is a part of life. I am teaching my children this and showing them healthy ways to cope with pain. What may be out of balance? This question helps me revisit my DIMs and SIMs.

Motherhood has given me the courage and strength to face my discomfort. It's allowing me to be aware, stay curious, and continue to learn and grow. I don't like having setbacks, but I now have healthy ways to cope with the setbacks. I know how to handle them better for me. I feel this is also helping me be the mother I want to be. I'm showing them, but I'm also changing and healing, and that's keeping me from placing my burdens on them. They do not need to carry my load for me. This is my work to do. I don't want my old stories to be theirs. My burdens are not for them to carry.

What is my body telling me? They will learn from me that it's brave to listen. Their bodies know. I will teach them healthy ways to cope with discomfort and tools they can try. This is a life skill that I'm proud I can teach them. Pain will show up at some point in their life, and to give them the tools to cope is something I'm happy and proud to do.

My pain has served a greater purpose, I'm seeing and understanding that now. I can forgive myself.

***

Forgiveness was a big piece of my healing. It allowed me to move forward. To forgive my young self, knowing that she did the best she could and there wasn't anything she did wrong. I was carrying this guilt, that it was my fault. *Why didn't I do this, or say this, or get help?* I would ruminate for days, and my body would get the weight of it. I learned that rumination could inhibit my medicine cabinet in my brain and my recurring negative thoughts or feelings can activate a pain response. My stomach would ache, my scalp would itch, my body would tighten up, and my breathing would be shallow. The key to my medicine cabinet was closed tight due to my rumination and thoughts.

The bottom of my feet would tingle and burn. The tingling would then move up to the back of my legs, thighs, and sides of my knees. *Is this plantar fasciitis? Is this my herniated disc? Do I have cancer? Maybe I need to see a doctor. Could this be multiple sclerosis?* My thoughts would race. I would feel these sensations in my body and think the worst. I would turn to Dr. Google just to see if my suspicion was correct and to validate my thinking. It was the worst thing to do, as I could find evidence to it all depending on what site I wanted to click on. I couldn't sleep, rethinking about it all. I was trying to change the outcome and thinking I could change the past.

Why can I forgive everyone but me? I would sit on my therapist's leather couch, pleading. My therapist reminded me that forgiveness is a choice I can give myself. Forgiveness only needs me, it's a gift for me. I found this so hard to do and believe. Again I had to be aware of my thoughts and beliefs and what I was telling myself. I wanted to forgive myself, and I wanted that gift. I needed permission to forgive myself and be kind. *I don't have to keep beating myself up anymore, that will not change the past.* I started practicing new thoughts and praying. *I'm becoming a woman who can forgive herself. God, please change me into a woman who can forgive herself.*

Chapter Nineteen
Thoughts Matter

Pain is real
I'm learning to feel
When I want to run
I sit in the sun
When I want to fight
Instead, I write
When I want to hide
I open my mind
Are my thoughts true?
Maybe a few
I get to decide
Which ones to leave behind
This is the power
I have every hour

I was taught that thoughts are physical things and that we often do not notice thoughts consciously. Our thoughts are chemically and physically in the brain; we can't just simply scrub them away. They are fixed loops. This is why pain recovery is not a quick fix. It takes time to change these loops, months and — for some — years. However, the great news is that once we gain new information, new experiences, and then take action, change begins.

My story is a great example. I would wake up, unable to move. Lying in bed, my mind would race.

Brain: Oh shit! The pain is back.

Me: Do not swear, that makes it worse.

Brain: Okay, Julie don't freak out! Try to breathe.

Me: Yes, breathe. This is pain you know, your great protector.

Brain: Shit. It better let me run. I'm in the middle of training.

Me: Stop saying shit! Breathe, remember to breathe.

Brain: Okay, okay, I'm breathing but we don't have time for this.

You can see how this can spiral very quickly into death and despair. This took a lot of practice to not let this go all day long. The negative thoughts used to consume me. I would get so mad at myself and my body.

What we say to ourselves during a setback matters. Jen Liddy of Jen Liddy Coaching & Development taught me to be aware of the thoughts I say to myself. She encouraged me to write out all the thoughts in my head, anything I was thinking, for five to ten minutes each day. This strategy really helped me gain self-awareness and insight into what I was saying to myself. This gave me the power to decide if I wanted to keep those thoughts or not. I would take one thought that I knew wasn't serving me and put it in the model she taught me. I could acknowledge that my pain was affected by my thoughts. My circumstance was the same — pain — but I was making it worse with my thoughts, which were creating feelings of shame, frustration, anxiety, or distress.

It made me think about running. What are my thoughts when I run and have pain? They are not, Shit, the pain is back. They are usually, Oh yeah, this is the part where I don't feel good but run anyway, or, This pain isn't harmful, or I know this discomfort is temporary. My thoughts about running in pain don't make me anxious or worried, so I keep running. The result is that I finish the race.

I used to think that I had to constantly brace my spine to prevent pain or a setback. I would think, *I have to tighten up more*, or *This pain must be because I forgot to brace my spine*. Though I continued to have setbacks, I wouldn't change these thoughts.

Why would I? I didn't have new information to change that thought, and I believed what I was doing was right. Plus, I didn't even realize how tense I was. It took me ten years to let this belief go. I had no idea how much of my pain persisted because of the thoughts and beliefs I was holding on to, nor did I initially realize how much of it was from my childhood.

***

The story I believed for so many years was that I need to be perfect at everything and shouldn't say or do anything wrong if I want to feel worthy, seen, and loved. You can imagine how hard this was to achieve.

Fear, in the form of my dad, would be sitting with me after basketball games, track meets, and cross-country races, implying that I'm no good and that I stink. *Why didn't you run faster? Why didn't you make more shots?* I was given the play-by-play of every negative thing possible! These negative messages filled my head, and they were all I could think about. It doesn't help that our brain is already biased toward negativity, so of course my thoughts were negative. The self-hatred started and these unhelpful thought patterns started to form, and the groove was getting deeper and deeper in my brain. *What is wrong with me?* it would scream.

For 20 years this thought pattern and narrative played out, and it wasn't until my life started to fall apart piece by piece that I got the courage to take a look. It's terrifying to look, it's hard. After desensitization therapy, I was ready to work on my thoughts. Gratefully I was guided by my coach, Jen, who is a ninja at this! Jen said, "Julie, the point of thought work is not to change all of your thoughts, it's to get to know what they are and whether you want to keep them." I was able to begin to acknowledge, accept, and allow these thoughts without judgment so I could decide.

There were so many thoughts I did not want to keep. The first ones that had to go were *What is wrong with me?* and *I don't know.* The thought pattern of *I don't know,* just made me more confused. What a dream stealer! *What is wrong with me?* made me feel like crap. *I don't want to be confused anymore, and I don't want to feel like crap all the time.*

"What do you want to think instead, or how do you want to feel?" Jen would ask me in our sessions. It was pretty frustrating when she asked me what I wanted to think instead. I had no idea! But I did know what I wanted to feel. I wanted to feel curious, calm, aware, and love. I wanted to love myself.

What do I need to think to feel like this instead? That was my work to do, but I couldn't do it alone. I'm so grateful I had my coach to help me get there and to teach me that I have 100% control over my thoughts. It certainly is a process and I had to be extra kind to myself, which was a challenge.

During our coaching sessions, my brain didn't like some of the thoughts, it quickly said, "No you don't," or, "That isn't true." I had to try on thoughts and see which ones I could believe or start to believe so my brain wouldn't immediately spiral into negativity again.

I started with, *I am learning how to love myself,* or *I'm exploring how to love myself.* I also liked, *Hello brain, I see your negative thoughts,* or *I know. I see you. I've got this.* These thoughts made me feel aware and curious. The power was now in my hands. I wanted to choose to believe these thoughts, so I practiced it every day and practiced finding positive evidence about myself. This didn't feel natural or easy for me at first, but I kept practicing. I decided I deserved it.

***

Knowing that I have 100% control of my thoughts during a setback has been a game-changer for me. The challenge became what to say to myself instead. I had so many deep grooves of unhelpful and outdated thinking on replay. I had believed those thoughts for so long that they were automatic. I wanted to unlearn these unhelpful thoughts and beliefs about myself and pain. I was embarrassed that I didn't know what to ask instead or what to say. I didn't know who I was. Jen was patient and kind during this process — and the best part was that I would leave our sessions feeling calm and confident. I'm so happy she was able to guide and coach me on how to get better at this. And for the first time, I felt this amazing relief and happiness. *I get to be who I want to be. I get to take charge of my life. No one can tell me what to think, that is 100% in my control.*

I don't want to think something is wrong with me, so what do I say instead when this thought comes up? Jen taught me an amazing model to help look at my thoughts and feelings in a way that I could understand. It was a significant step in my pain recovery. It was another tool that put me in the driver's seat and gave me the power.

It was an active strategy to help myself, not a passive one. That is what I wanted. I wanted to be in charge of my story, no longer a victim. I will not take the back seat in my life. Two thoughts I tried on and loved how they made me feel were: "There's nothing that's gone wrong here," and "I have a choice." Those thoughts are true and helpful for me. And when I say those thoughts, I feel empowered and calm. It stops me from ruminating and freaking out. My discomfort doesn't get worse. It gives me the space to take action and get the results I want.

Running, lifting weights, and having moments of no pain were the results I was starting to notice. To get to the Boston Marathon, I recognized the importance of retraining my brain, changing my thoughts and beliefs that were not serving me anymore, and coaching. I was all in. Our brain is amazing, thank you, Jesus. We truly are fearfully and wonderfully made!

***

When it happens, the pain stops me in my tracks and comes on like a jolt, without warning. It tries to knock me

down, send me to the floor. Yet I manage to stay standing.
It brings tears to my eyes, and I try not to let anyone see,
especially my children. I feel tingling and burning down
my legs into my feet, the sharp twist of pain in my low
back, and knots in my stomach. I freeze, hoping it will let
up. This sends me into a spiral of rumination and terrible
self-talk. *What did I do wrong? Why is this still happening? I
hate this.* These questions are dead ends and make me feel
worse, only increasing my pain.

I don't want my children to see me in pain. I don't want to
lose my temper or tell them, "No, I can't sit on the floor
with you," or, "No, I can't run around outside." I would
get so frustrated. *I'm not the mom they deserve.* Would they
think I couldn't take care of them? Would this negatively
affect them, they are so young? Would they think I wasn't a
good mother?

I wanted to be a great mother, but this pressure to be
perfect and hide the pain from them only made my pain
worse. My back would tighten up more. I wouldn't focus
on my breath, and I would hide in my closet to cry. My
thoughts were spirally out of control. *You shouldn't be a
mom; you can't handle it. You are going to be just like your dad.*

These thoughts were so painful. I decided to question
them. I realized they were not true, just old stories coming
back up. My therapist had me write down what being a
great mom looked like for me. How would I know? It was
the best advice. I wrote down what I think a great mom

does or says. I looked at the list and to my surprise, I was doing a lot of it. Of course, there is always room for improvement and growth, but I was a good enough mom. Being honest with my children about my pain actually strengthened our connection. I was healing old wounds, rewriting old stories, learning to cope in healthy ways, and my children were witnessing it. I was showing them a different way of living, living from a place of compassion, understanding, forgiveness, and love. This is the work I'm committed to not only for my children but for myself.

I don't want to hide from them or pretend that everything is okay. Life sometimes is not okay. I want them to be able to handle the miserable bits and I want to show them some healthy ways to cope in those times. I want to teach them about their thoughts and feelings. It's important to feel and to be self-aware. *What can I learn from this setback?* This is the question I ask myself today. Saying this instead keeps me curious and calm.

***

There is no protocol for this, no special supplement or treatment. We are all unique, and what works for me may not work for you. However, one thing that's true for us all is that there is no endpoint to healing. I've learned to accept that pain, negative thoughts, or feelings will show up in my life. The difference now is my reaction and management of my mind. The old Julie would beat herself up, not sleep, and ruminate for weeks. Now I'll dump it out on paper and find some helpful thoughts to say. *I can handle any emotion that comes up. I have the tools in place. I know what to do.* Then I move on to my action plan. This is a skill I'm practicing, just like running. I want to get better at it so I work on it daily, knowing that some days will be shitty, some days I will fail. I don't have to make it mean I'm not worthy or I'm not lovable, it means I'm human.

I can be triggered by words, actions, or someone's presence and I have to stop and ask, "Why am I being triggered right now?" Then I can sit with it and feel it. This is still the hardest thing for me because the go-to thoughts are *I thought I was over this, I thought I dealt with this already,* or *Why is this still triggering me?* I want to blame myself, but I know that doesn't serve me. I catch that thought and remind myself that there is nothing that's gone wrong here, stay curious.

That thought is what stops my spiral. There is nothing that's gone wrong here. When I can come from a place of curiosity, non-judgment, and hold space for myself, I'm better able to sit and decide what it was that triggered me and what I need to address. Is there something that needs to be reconciled? What I discover from this is then my responsibility. What can I do to help myself move through this discomfort? This is what I have control over.

I'm grateful for the support I had and still have. This work is not to be done alone and there is no end to growth or learning. I thought there was an endpoint, a finish line. I've arrived and done the badass work so no more negative thoughts, pain, or crappy feelings, right? I laugh now at that belief. I know that was just my perfectionism coming out, the liar telling me that fear won't show up, my inner critic will go crawl in a hole never thinking a negative thought again, and my great pain protector will take a vacation. This was hard for me to accept. My belief was if the pain, negative thoughts, or crappy feelings returned it was my fault or something was wrong with me. This was not true, and it was a belief that was holding me back in my pain recovery and healing. I was glad to have a therapist who gently challenged this belief. She reminded me that I'm human and there is no finish line to this work. She said, "You will continue to grow, change, and learn and that is being human. You are normal. There is nothing wrong with you."

She was honest with me and not someone who said, "I can fix you," because that's just nonsense. No one is going to fix me, and no one is going to fix you. I get to take personal responsibility for all of me, no one else, and that is badass! Yes, it's terrifying, but I bet if you look at yourself in the mirror, deep down you know exactly what you have to do. Be the expert, take ownership of your challenges, and own your story. You get to write it. It's your road.

Chapter Twenty
Second Chance

Stars are shining bright
Staring at the great big sky
I could stay in bed
Glad I love to run instead
Outside time to clear my head

I looked at the time clock. The bold red numbers read 3:37:43. I ran under 3:40:00. *I just qualified for the Boston Marathon. I did it!* I couldn't hide my smile, which stretched from ear to ear. My loud and proud runners' hair expressed grit and persistence. My discomfort and thirst suddenly disappeared. I stood in awe of what my body had just accomplished. All the hard work paid off, from the coaching, the therapy, to the training. I had come so far, and this day captured it all.

Loud and proud finish at Fargo Marathon 2017

I wanted to hug someone, but no one was there. My family didn't make the trip out with me. Jeff stayed home with the kids so I could make the trip to Fargo, North Dakota. It was a flat course and they said it was a great Boston qualifier race. They were right! I quickly found my bag so I could call Jeff and let him know. I was so excited to tell him. I couldn't wait to get home to show them the medal. It was a huge round medal with the words "Finisher" engraved on it. This was just as much their medal as it was mine. Training for a marathon takes support from everyone, and I couldn't thank my family enough for sticking with me through it all.

I would leave early every Saturday for two or three hours. Jeff would take care of the kids while I was gone. After his week of working, I truly appreciated him getting up early on Saturdays. My family's support in 2017 allowed me to qualify for the second time to get to Boston. I was certain this was it. My dream of finally racing Boston would be achieved in April 2018.

When registration day came in September 2017, I was pumped. I opened up the form on the computer, submitted my qualifying time, and anxiously waited to hear back from the Boston Athletic Association. I've learned over the years that even if you qualify, it doesn't guarantee you a spot. I knew there was a slight chance that my age group would fill fast, yet I stayed optimistic. I was certain I was heading to Boston. I was already making plans and telling my family. I was confident that my time was fast enough to get me in.

A few weeks later I was standing in the kitchen when I received the email. My heart sank. I was wrong. I was 18 seconds too slow. I read the email over and over hoping it was a mistake. It stated that I didn't get in. My dream of heading to Boston would not happen in 2018, after all. It was an awful sting. The pain, sadness, and disappointment consumed me. *I didn't run fast enough. I can't believe it.* I tried to catch my thoughts from spiraling. I knew my inner critic was going to have a field day with this news.

I sat alone in my room with all my thoughts and feelings. I cried, I breathed, and I allowed myself to just feel it all. I sat quietly. I heard my courage whisper to me, *You will get to Boston, don't give up on yourself, keep going.*

I was a little worn out mentally after the Fargo Marathon
and recognized it. I decided I wanted a coach to help me
get to Boston. I needed someone in my corner to support
me and keep me going. I wanted a coach I could trust. I
also felt like I was running out of time, especially with this
diagnosis of psoriatic arthritis. *How much longer will my
body be able to run?* That thought entered my mind and I
rolled my eyes. *My mind can be such a downer.*

I linked up with Joel Sattgast of Zeren Physical Therapy
and Performance Coaching. We talked over the phone
about my goals, expectations, my health, and we seemed to
be a good fit. I was glad he could work with me, and I was
determined to stick with his training plan.

Joel planned my training runs and strength program, and
inserted rest days, yoga days, and fitness walking into the
mix. I loved it! I showed up every day and eagerly did
what was scheduled. It was one less thing I had to think
about, which was awesome! More brain juice for the other
things, like positive self-talk, meditation, and mothering.

My training runs were fun, set up mainly by minutes
instead of miles. This had my mind engaged differently
and I liked that. I was starting to see a change in my ability,
not only physically but mentally. The way Joel coached me
was collaborative and supportive. His language was
positive and encouraging. I wanted my language to reflect
this and it's what I was reading about: mindset. How we
talk to ourselves matters. What we say affects us

physically, and I made the connection that my thoughts were a big piece to my pain challenge. It was reassuring to have a coach who understood this and who believed this too. I felt safe, that I could talk to him and not be laughed at or questioned negatively.

I reflected on high school and college racing. When my mind was positive and focused, so was my running. I thought back to races I won and lost, races in which I performed well and races I didn't. What was different? My mind. My mind was what needed to be trained, daily just like running. I was starting to see that more clearly. The more I read about the brain, mindset, and self-help books geared to positive thinking and performance, the more I realized how much power I have. No one can tell me what to think, it's always my choice one hundred percent. This tool of thought work and training my mind was making the difference, not only in my running but in all areas of my life.

I truly believed that, with Joel's coaching plan, support, and training focusing on my mind and my thoughts, Boston was already achieved. I would be there in 2020 without a doubt. It was an amazing feeling, and I could see how my thoughts were creating that. It's hard to believe that for over eight years I could hardly run three miles if I ran at all.

Now I'm here! I'm back to running despite my pain setbacks and on my way to a Boston Qualifier.

My alarm goes off. It's 4:21 a.m. I'm three months into my training for the Wineglass Marathon. Some days it's hard to lace up and get out the door. It's so dark and cold. I want to hide back under the covers. My mind starts.

Maybe I can run later today. My back feels so stiff, maybe I should wait.

My thoughts are already trying to talk me out of it. There goes my mind again. I know the pattern. A pep talk is needed. Managing my mind is becoming a daily practice. I'm getting better at recognizing the thoughts that aren't serving me and finding ones that will.

You'll feel better after moving, you always do. It's a beautiful morning, let's go see the stars.

I step out of bed and put on the running clothes that I had laid out the night before. This is a trick I do, the faster I get dressed the less time my mind has to talk me out of it.

See, I'm ready. Time to run.

It's when I'm pounding the pavement, I do my best thinking. It's quiet, the stars are out; it's just me and my thoughts. I download the day and what I want to get done. I sing songs and write books in my head. It's my time, and as a mother of two small children, it's required time. I recognize if I don't get up and move, my pain is louder and I'm short with my children. This training isn't just about Boston, it's also about motherhood. My children don't deserve a cranky mother, and I have control over that. When I get out of bed and run or walk, my pain is better. Some days it's gone! Getting out of bed before they get up is a priority. I'm ready. I can be the mother I want to be. It's not easy, but training for a marathon is training for life.

***

Every Saturday morning, my friend Felicia and I meet for a training run. I'm so grateful to have a friend who enjoys running as much as I do. She's a marathoner too. We talk about running, life, health, and our goals. It's in the dark morning runs where we both hold space for each other to share some challenging things we have overcome and what we have learned. I can resonate with her struggles and setbacks. I wasn't alone. These training runs built us into stronger runners and friends. She's helped me stay accountable, calls me out when I need it most, and makes two hours of running seem like ten minutes. I can't thank her enough for showing up each morning with me snow, rain, or shine. We have fun and laugh. Running friends are the best.

We joked as we stepped outside. The temperature was 5 degrees Fahrenheit and the snow hit our eyelashes. We were crazy to be out here, yet we were committed to getting our run in. The wind was fierce that morning, whipping my ponytail to the side and hitting my face, which already felt numb five minutes into the run. I wanted to turn back around and get into my warm car.

That was an option. *No one is forcing me to run. I'm out here because I want to get to Boston and my dream is stronger than the warm car. I will keep showing up. I will bring a good attitude.* My thoughts turned to: *Look at the snow and the lake. It's beautiful, and I get to see it. I'm running again.* I felt an enormous amount of gratitude and appreciation as Felicia was there running with me.

Running buddies

We came to the turnaround point and headed back the way we came. We had the wind at our backs. I felt this new energy inside of me. Two runners were coming our way.

"I guess we aren't the only crazy ones." I laughed, turning to Felicia. She laughed as we both picked up our pace a little. "We are kinda badass, like those navy seals," I said. We both laughed, as we just finished reading David

Goggins's book, *Can't Hurt Me: Master Your Mind and Defy the Odds*. It was an amazing, inspiring story showing the true power of the human mind and what we are capable of. This book was giving me more evidence that I was going in the right direction by training my mind. The weather was helping us build that mental toughness. It was great practice, and we ran a half marathon that day! BOOYAH!

Chapter Twenty-One
God is Faithful

Boston Marathon here I come
many years to achieve this one
will keep on training
my mind is gaining
I'm running the roads as I hum

I get on the bus, feeling like a high school kid. Where should I sit, closer to the front or the back? Who should I sit with? I spot another woman close to my age and I slide in next to her. She's on her phone so I don't bother to make small talk. My phone is back at the hotel. I don't want to be distracted.

The bus is rather quiet as we head to the start line. I look outside, raindrops hitting one by one against the window. I begin to recall memories from my high school cross-country races. I had some of my best runs in the rain. I like running in the rain, I'm going to run well today. I hear some of the other runners on the bus groan about the weather because it wasn't supposed to rain. They weren't calling for rain today, but I don't entertain those thoughts at all. I'm busy recalling all the reasons why I love racing in the rain. The sound relaxes me, the drops hitting my face, cleaning the sweat away from my eyes, and with every step water splashing up against my legs reminding me I'm alive. I am a runner.

My mindset matters as I head into this race. I've been training my mind just as much as my body for this marathon. If I consider just one negative thought for too long, things generally go downhill. I've been practicing redirecting my mind to something true or helpful. I can spiral to thoughts like "I'm not good enough" very easily or "This pain isn't supposed to be here." I know this all too well in all areas of my life, not just running. That's why getting to this point in my training is such a big damn deal for me. For over 20 years I've listened to every negative thought in my head and believed it. I never thought to consider, is this true? Is this helpful or outdated?

This mentality created a life of self-doubt, self-hatred, and pain challenges that I would need to face instead of running from. What a long journey it has been. I knew this was just the beginning. I had turned a corner, though, and as I rode the bus to the start line, I felt free.

I step off the bus, watching runners striding up and down the road getting ready for the start. I head over to the porta-potty. I had gone to the bathroom before I got on the bus, yet my pre-race nerves have already started. I wait in line, repeating to myself, I'm ready. The weather and course are perfect. I'm going to have a great race.

I search for the pace group as I get closer to the start line. I see a tall, muscular yet slim blond hair man holding a sign: Eight-minute/mile pace. That's me. I need to stay with him and the group. As I join them, I hear many of the runners talking about Boston and how the qualifying time just changed. We have to run even faster to qualify, and they made the change today. I overheard the conversation, but I'm determined to not let their thoughts change my thinking. That's okay, I can run that fast. I stay focused and confident. I've got this, all I have to do is stay with the pacer.

This is it. My try again to qualify for the Boston Marathon. I feel nervous. I huddle in close to the pack of runners as we toe the start line. We are all after a Boston Qualifier (BQ) time and knowing this gives me a feeling of safety and reassurance. Stay with this group and I will get the time I need. Our excitement grows as we get behind the pacer. I just need to stick with this group, I can do this. I keep repeating over and over, I am a strong runner. I got this. I bend down to check that my sneakers are double knotted, and my watch is ready to go.

The drizzle of rain falls on my arms. The sound relaxes me and drowns out all the chatter of the runners. I get ready for the gun to go off. I run well in the rain. This is a positive affirmation I repeat, and it's easy to believe. My childhood memories of racing in the rain start to take shape in my mind, I did race well in the rain. I take a deep breath. My mind is different, it surprises me. It's stronger, kinder, and more alert.

At mile ten the pain started. *So soon?!* I thought. My right hip was getting my attention and my first thought was, *I better slow down.* I quickly recognized this as my brain just trying to keep me safe. *I'm okay. I do not need to slow down, there is nothing that has gone wrong here, I'm running hard.* This discomfort wasn't new, and I recognized it. I shook out my arms and focused on the pacer's back. *Just stay right here, you can do this.*

By mile 16 my hip started getting less and less attention from me as my focus stayed on the group. I got this surge of energy and confidence; I was sticking with the pace. I kept coaching myself as I ran, remembering the thoughts to help me stay focused and positive. *I will do this. I am a strong runner. I got this, don't back down. Don't let up, stay relaxed.*

At mile 20, the pacer casually asked, "How are you all feeling?" Some of us said great, really great. He replied, "Go see how many runners you can catch. Go race now. GO! GO! GO!"

I don't know what came over me, but I went! I went with the other runners. I kept my focus ahead and repeated to myself, *Keep your eyes ahead and start catching as many runners as you can.* I was so focused. I was in the zone. My legs were running so fast, but I felt I wasn't in control anymore. My pain was there but somehow, I paid no attention to it. My focus was on catching as many people as I could. Each runner I passed increased my confidence and my pace felt faster. *Let's see how many runners I can catch.* My mind shifted to this task. I continued to keep my eyes ahead on the runners in front of me.

"GO, GO!" a woman in my group shouted behind me. I don't know how she knew but that encouragement shot through my body, and I took off toward the finish, my arms pumping, my heart pounding, my legs moving like someone else had taken over.

Wineglass Marathon Finish 2018

The finish was in view and all I kept thinking was, *Go, go, don't back down.* I crossed the line catching a glimpse of the clock; it read 3:27:04. *Holy Sh*t! I did it!* The tears flowed as

I saw my family. My mom hugged me, and I cried, "I did it, Mom, I did it!" I grabbed my husband and kids in pure joy. Everything clicked: my heart, mind, and body. I ran the race of my life. *I am capable. I am a strong runner.*

With the time of 3:27:04, I was accepted into the 124th Boston Marathon! *For years I've dreamed about this race and now I will be there in 2020. YAAAAAHOOOOOO!* It was going to be amazing. As I danced around the kitchen with my children shouting, "We're going to Boston! We're going to Boston!"

Boston qualifier at Wineglass Marathon 2018 with family

My smile stretched from one end of the room to the other. The words on my computer screen read, "Congratulations, you are accepted into the 124th Boston Marathon." I never gave up. I never gave up. The years of therapy, coaching, reading, searching, and pushing courage through the setbacks. The hard work paid off. The dream that started when I was 21 years old was finally coming true at forty!

I give my 21-year-old self a high-five and a gigantic hug as we cry happy tears, jumping up and down together. Thank you for showing up even through the pain and depression. Thank you for finding a way even when you wanted to hide and give up. Thank you for running. You made it!

The plan was to continue to train with my coach until the race on April 20, 2020. My coach encouraged me to run another marathon between now and then so I would continue to develop the skill of racing. I chose something closer to home, The Rochester Marathon on Sept 22, 2019. Getting up at 4:30 a.m. felt different this time. I was gaining confidence in myself, my running ability, and I was feeling stronger. Even though my right hip would ache and sting, and my left foot would throb during my training runs, I recognized this discomfort. I would listen and slow down or walk for a bit if that's what my body was saying. The biggest thing I noticed was how I spoke to myself. I was kinder and talking to myself like I would a friend. This was hard work for me and a daily practice so much like running. They go hand in hand. *What's my run today? What am I going to say to myself today?* I was being deliberate with my thoughts and my words.

My goal for the Rochester Marathon was to run a 3:25:00 race. My training for the most part had been solid since my

Boston Qualifier, and I was handling my discomfort with no major setbacks. My nutrition had improved as well, and I was feeling good overall. I had this new sense of confidence and pride in my running, and I believed that I could run even faster.

However, I had no control over the weather, and I wasn't prepared for it. It was hot — unbelievably hot for a September marathon. It was 90 degrees Fahrenheit, and I worried about hydration and pace as I toed the line. *Do I stick with the plan my coach and I talked about, or do I start slower? Have I had enough to drink?* My self-doubt started to creep in, and I could feel my body tensing up. I shook my arms out and took some deep breaths. *I can do this.*

Sweat was dripping in my eyes, and the sun beat down on me. A memory of unloading hay wagons on the farm suddenly popped into my head. The feeling of the hot sun, sweat, and achiness all came flooding into my mind — not a memory I wanted to recall at this moment. I found that distance running does this. My mind shuffles around from old memories to songs, to thoughts. It's the thoughts that take over my running, particularly the ones that are not true or helpful. I found that racing these last few years brought this to the forefront and it was something I wanted to improve on. I wanted to manage my mind during running just like I was in my everyday life. I was seeing the progress, and I was able to breathe and respond how I wanted. I was able to show up instead of reacting. Reacting is what I learned as a child, and I did not want to be like that.

I want to have self-control and self-awareness, two things that I was not shown. I want to show these to my children so it's my job to learn this and practice this skill. Thank goodness it's a skill and not a genetic default.

***

I was at mile ten, craving a gallon size jug of water instead of the paper cup handed to me. I was so thirsty. I was already out of the hydration that I was carrying, which was supposed to get me to mile 14! I was starting to panic as I saw the turn-off point for the half marathoners. Briefly, I entertained the thought of heading that way instead. *Oh Julie you can't, Jeff and the kids are handing off more bottles at mile 14, you have to keep going.* I didn't want to let down my coach or my family. I knew if I didn't finish, I would feel humiliation and embarrassment. *Plus, I won't get the marathon medal. Keep moving!*

I shuffled on, literally. My legs just wouldn't move, I felt like someone was pulling me down to the ground, wanting me to sit, wanting me to stop, wanting me to give up. I just couldn't pick up the pace or get myself to change it up, but I wasn't going to give up. *Okay,* I thought, *let me just get to them.* I slowed down my pace little by little and of course, I was beating myself up about it. *Julie, get moving, this pace will not get you the time you want.* I yelled at myself. Then something surprising happened. I walked! Can you believe it, I walked? I had never walked in a marathon, but I did that day, more than once. Horror! Shock! And you know what, no one yelled at me, not even me! I did my best and decided with the weather I would finish and not beat myself up anymore. *I will enjoy the crowd, encourage the other runners who pass me and just run. This won't be the day for personal records, it will be the day I finish and not yell at myself for the next fourteen miles, promising I won't beat myself up when I cross the finish.*

I raced terribly compared to the Wineglass Marathon but was surprised to finish under four hours. Even with all the walking, I did not do badly. It was still difficult because deep down I wanted to run a 3:30:00 marathon again. I started to beat myself up, and imposter syndrome was calling my name. Did I still deserve to go to Boston? Could I call myself a sub 3:30:00 marathoner? How could I run the race of my life just a year ago and then today run so dreadfully?

Then my adult brain stepped in. Okay, you've beat yourself up long enough. You finished, you did it! This is a time many strive for, don't discount what you accomplished today in the heat. I looked at my kids, husband, my sister-in-law, and her children who came to cheer me on. They hugged me and congratulated me. They recognized how hot it was to run and commended me on my finish. My children's eyes gazed at the shiny medal hanging from my neck and were eager to wear it. Their little hands reached out to touch it. I stopped my thoughts of self-doubt and promised to talk kindly to myself and turn my mood around.

Julie, this is racing. This is life. It doesn't always go our way, even when we do everything right. The marathon and my pain experience have taught me that. What now? I show my children that when life knocks you down, you get back up. You keep going. Boston Marathon here we come!

***

After the Rochester Marathon, my lack of confidence suffocated me. Would I be able to run another sub 3:30:00 marathon? Did I belong in Boston after such a miserable race? My mind was spiraling out of control with self-doubt and defeat. My focus on my negative racing experience just a few months ago consumed me.

I'm glad I shared this with my coach, Joel. He was someone I could trust. A pep talk to shift my mindset was needed! Our conversation went something like this: "Julie, I want you to think about the Wineglass Marathon. Everything clicked for you that day. Recall that moment and how you felt when you finished. Now think about this marathon. The Rochester marathon is an outlier, you know what you are capable of."

I stood in my kitchen with the phone held to my ear. I closed my eyes and brought myself back to the Wineglass Marathon. I had qualified for Boston and achieved a personal record. I visualized the start, the race, the finish. It was clear as day. The inside of me grinned from head to toe.

A year ago I ran the marathon of my life. My mind visualized the Wineglass Marathon from start to finish, and this overwhelming feeling of joy squashed the self-doubt. I realized that I could feel joy any time I wanted by simply remembering that day and remembering that marathon finish. I had the power to create this feeling. I laughed to myself. Why would I continue to think about this negative marathon experience when I had the memory of Wineglass so easily accessible to me? Isn't that the power we all have?

This was another "aha!" moment for me in my healing. Why continue to relive the negative experiences when they make me feel miserable, sad, and defeated? I'm creating undue suffering by thinking about the past. I don't need to keep going back there. I can't change it. I take what I can learn and move on. It sounds so easy, but it was the hardest shift for me to make. I had to be deliberate with my thinking on a daily basis, and I still do. Managing my mind is a practice. It's a skill I can get better at, and I want to. The model that Jen Liddy taught me was the tool for me to get better at this.

Chapter Twenty-Two
Wheat was the Contender

I was born to run and not eat gluten
My toe swollen, red, and tender
Wheat was the contender
I learned the truth and gave gluten the booten
Hallelujah, no more pain, I ditched the gluten

I look down at my feet as I step out of the shower. My left big toe is bright red, swollen, and stiff, but my right toe is not. I've seen this big toe redness and swelling before; my toe looks like my dad's. A memory from my childhood resurfaces of my dad sitting on the couch watching TV barefoot. I walked by and accidentally hit his toe. He yelled out in pain, angry at me for not paying attention to where I was walking. My eyes darted to the floor, my head down, shoulders slouched as I apologized. My stomach clenched. I thought, Julie, why didn't you watch where you were going? You're so stupid, now Dad is mad at you. He probably won't talk to you now.

I hadn't meant to hurt him, but I understand now why he reacted the way he did. He was in pain. My heart swelled with compassion and empathy, as my foot looks the same as his. *Is this something I will just have to live with? I've learned*

*from my siblings that dad has had multiple surgeries. Is that
what will happen to me? No, I don't want to believe that story. I
am not my dad, I am Julie. I will keep pushing courage and figure
this out.*

I went to my doctor and got an EKG. I wanted to make sure
my heart was healthy and if there was anything I needed to
do now to be proactive. My doctor said I was healthy and
doing great, and he recommended I keep running and
eating well. I was doing both things consistently but the
redness in my toe was still there. I was told it was psoriatic
arthritis, but I still felt this nudge inside of me that it
wasn't. They offered me medications, again. I was
persistent. *Not yet,* I thought. *I don't want to do medications if
there is something I can do instead to help myself.* I kept
researching and reading. I stopped eating refined sugar,
processed foods, and dairy completely. My psoriasis
cleared up so that it was visible only on my right elbow,
but my toe did not change.

I signed up for Dr. Joe Tatta's 12-week functional nutrition
course and dug deeper. It was an eye-opener for me. One
thing in the course that stood out was this statement, "If
you have pain, you must take out gluten." *That's me.* That
was all I needed to hear to take action. I had to give it a go
and find out for myself. I eliminated gluten (so I thought)
for three months before reintroducing it to see if this was
affecting my pain.

I bought gluten-free waffles for a quick post-run breakfast, switched to gluten-free pasta, and continued with no refined sugars, processed foods, corn, and dairy. I still bought bread for my family. My children love toast, and we have one toaster. I toasted my gluten-free waffles and their bread (wheat, gluten) in the same toaster. I didn't think that this was a problem. It never dawned on me that the gluten from their bread was getting on my gluten-free waffles. Duh, it was!

Maybe this is why for months I never saw a change in my toe symptoms. And because I wasn't seeing a change in my symptoms, I would cheat. Some days I would eat gluten and some days I wouldn't. I wasn't ever 100% gluten-free. Deep down I believed that it wasn't a real contributor to my pain, so I cheated now and then. I was wrong. There is joy in being wrong.

We were heading to the Adirondack mountains for a few days, and there was the best bagel shop there. I decided I would reintroduce gluten there every morning, fabulous and delicious. What a SIM for me — I was eating gluten, had no increase in symptoms, and thinking gluten wasn't a problem for me. Then BOOM! Three days later and I was having a massive setback, the worst one I'd had in a long time.

The neuroimmune system can have a delayed response, and I think I was experiencing an immune response to the gluten. This setback came at the end of July 2020 just two

months before I was scheduled to race the Boston
Marathon. I could hardly move, I had sores all in my
mouth, and stomach pain that had me rolled up on my
side! It was the moment Delaney, my five-year-old
daughter, had to put on my socks for me that I knew it was
gluten. I heard the whisper, and it was confident and kind.
Hey Julie, it's the gluten, you need to stop eating it. I listened,
and I don't use the family toaster anymore.

I went to the dentist that week to have my teeth cleaned
and to look at my mouth. He asked me what was going on
and I just dumped everything out, the joint pain, the mouth
sores, the reintroduction of gluten and he confirmed what I
was thinking. I think it helped that he could relate to my
situation, as he shared with me, he was diagnosed with
celiac. He told me to go off gluten completely, and he
mentioned the toaster! I needed to have my own toaster. I
laughed because I didn't realize how important that was.

Gluten was a contributor after all and a huge piece to my
pain experience that I never would have considered if it
wasn't for Dr. Joe Tatta's functional nutrition course. It was
an eye-opener and proved to me just how much nutrition,
the food we put into our bodies, matters. I took out all
processed foods, refined sugar, dairy, corn, and finally, I
took out gluten.

Now when I get out of the shower and look down at my
feet I smile, almost in disbelief. My left foot now looks
exactly like my right foot. The redness is gone, the stiffness

and swelling are no longer present. When I run, my left foot feels loose, happy, and free. A new sense of empowerment comes over me. I did this, I took ownership and figured it out at my pace. They say it is psoriatic arthritis, but now I'm beginning to think that this is wrong too.

I decided to hold off on challenging the diagnosis of psoriatic arthritis until after the Boston Marathon. I didn't want this to change my focus or distract me in any way. My goal was to run the Boston Marathon no matter what. My dream would be achieved. I was sticking to the plan. Onward and upward!

Chapter Twenty-Three
Boston Marathon 2020

A running buddy
Talk, laugh, and cheer each other on
So grateful for her

When the COVID-19 pandemic hit in March 2020, my
dream of racing the Boston Marathon for the first time
became uncertain. The race was scheduled for April 20, but
news broke that it would be postponed to September 2020.
With all the chaos, loss, and day-to-day changes that were
taking place, I was doubtful. I don't know how the world
should be, but this was not how I imagined it. It was
heartbreaking and scary. I decided for my mental health to
stay off the news and social media sites.

I leaned on my faith and focused on the things I could
control. I continued training with my friend Felicia in
hopes that the Boston Marathon would take place. I held
onto this goal so I would keep going. It gave me stability
and routine, which I desperately needed. I would use
running to keep my spirits up and my sanity. As a mother
of two young children, running makes me a better mother.
Boston or not, I would keep running. Every Saturday
morning Felicia and I would meet to run, laugh, and vent

about our struggles. I'm so grateful we both had each other during this time to lean on.

When we found out that Boston was indeed canceled, I was disappointed, but I reminded myself that it was just a race. It was a race that I could try for again. I had waited this long; I could wait some more. Besides, the priority in the world was much bigger than a marathon. The Boston Athletic Association (B.A.A.) understood that and a virtual race for 2020 was announced. The email went on to say, "That all participants have the opportunity to participate in the virtual alternative to the 124th Boston Marathon, which can be run any time between September 7-14, 2020. Participants in the virtual 2020 Boston Marathon will be required to complete the 26.2-mile distance within a six-hour time period and provide proof of timing to the B.A.A."

I was hesitant to register. *It won't be the same. Do I want to do this?* I admit I was disappointed, but in a way amused by it all. I started to laugh. After all these years of trying to get to Boston, how ironic that this would happen. I wouldn't have had it any other way, it was building my resilience and that was always what I was striving for.

I registered for the Virtual Race and needed to pivot my plan. I was not going to let this pandemic throw me off course of my goal. I was in, and so was Felicia! She was excited, and Sam, another friend, was on board too. Awesome, I had two running buddies who would go the distance with me. I didn't think much of it. I could race it alone, but when race day came the importance of my friends and family supporting me, cheering me on brought new meaning to racing.

We planned our virtual marathon on The Erie Canal Trail, flat and fast, with not much foot or car traffic to manage. A beautiful course with a combination of paved and gravel paths, beautiful trees, and a waterway. We would run out and back, turning around at 13 miles. This would allow us to set up our hydration stops along the way. It would allow family and friends to support us as we covered the distance. We scheduled the race for September 12, 2020. The day before, we took sidewalk chalk and made our makeshift Boston start and finish line. I was getting excited. The pre-race jitters were already starting, even for a virtual race. My goal was to run as I did at Wineglass, with a finish time of 3:30:00. I didn't think my setback just five weeks prior would affect me enough to change my approach. I felt good.

Start-Finish Ready for Virtual Boston Marathon 2020

My mind was more concerned and anxious about the logistics. I needed to start my watch and the app on my phone so my coach, family, and friends could track me as I ran. I needed to provide my results to the B.A.A. as proof of finishing and wanted the time to be accurate. Remember, I'm a recovery perfectionist. I was getting anxious about it. I don't train or run with my phone, so this was new, and I didn't practice. This is one rule I follow, don't eat, drink, or do anything new the day before or on race day. Well, carrying my phone was something new and it was freaking me out. I know it may sound silly, but it was a big distraction the morning of the race. *How will I start my watch and the phone at the same time?* It was ridiculous. This thought was not helping me, and my nerves were on edge. Did it matter if I started my phone a few seconds after my watch? Of course not, but I couldn't get my brain to settle down.

It was dark as I pulled into the parking lot to the entrance of the trail. Sam and Felicia joined me as we jogged up to the start line. They were so talkative and relaxed, and I wanted to mirror their mood. I took some deep breaths and reminded myself to have fun, enjoy this moment and be proud. *I trained so hard for this; I am ready. Today's the day I run the Boston Marathon, a dream I've been striving for. It's here, I made it! I will finally be able to join this group of marathoners and make history in the process.*

It was just about 6 a.m. I wanted to start on time. My uncle and aunt would be waiting at the one-and-a-half-mile mark at 6:15 a.m. to cheer us on. I didn't want them to wait. I got my phone out and made sure the app was up and running. I then got my watch set to start. "Okay, ready guys, let's go!" I hit my watch then started to run. I hit the start on my phone and shoved it in my running vest pocket, fumbling a little to zip it up. A sigh of relief came over me. I didn't drop the phone, and it appeared to be tracking us. Ironically, after the race, I learned the app stopped tracking us at mile two. No one knew where we were. After all that worry and anxiety I carried, it didn't work. What a great lesson learned; the phone has no place for me in a race. It stays in the car next time.

We were off! Three runners heading down the dark paved trail to achieve something that none of us thought would be possible this year. Sam was setting a good pace at around an eight-minute mile pace, and I figured we would pick it up as we got going. My goal was to run at 7:55 pace most of the race then pick it up with the last six miles to go. I had my plan, now I just needed to execute it. We had perfect weather and a flat course. There was no reason I couldn't run the time I planned.

We heard a bell ring as we got closer to the one-and-a-half-mile mark. I could make out two shadows in the distance. My uncle Tim and aunt Colleen had made it! They started cheering as we passed them. I smiled and yelled, "Thank you!" It was such a great feeling to have some support so early on. We made our way across the road and back on the gravel trail. At mile six my mom would be waiting with hydration. I would switch out an empty bottle for a full one to place in my running vest. I took a look at my watch, making sure we were on pace. *I'm running too slow.* I started to pick up the pace a bit, but I was not on my target pace. I could feel my body starting to tense up. This feeling of disappointment washed over me because my legs weren't moving as fast as I thought. *Crap, I gotta get moving.*

I could already feel my right hip starting to nag at me, this achiness creeping in already at mile five. *That's not good.* I quickly brought my focus back to Sam and Felicia and what they were talking about. My training has been solid, but my mind can still run away from me if I'm not alert and focused. It's like a wild animal, darting around from one thought to the next, untamed, and hard to catch. Those thoughts don't just sit up there in my mind, they creep down into my body, and my hip stings, back tenses, and my stomach clenches. This discomfort early on was connected to my thoughts and anxiety about the logistics, from starting my watch, worrying that my family won't be at the mile marks for hydration swapping, and wondering if we would cover the right mileage. My guess is that it was triggering this pain response early on. This is how my pain experience can show up. My thoughts can trigger these feelings in my body. *This is not pain that's damaging, but it's still pain.* I shook out my arms and focused on my breath. I *can do this, I see you brain, relax. We are safe.* As we approached mile six, I saw my mom. A feeling of relief washed over me; she was there like she said. Maybe I could count on my mom.

An old story from childhood had me questioning my own mother's reliability. Waiting in the parking lot to be picked up after school, my stomach aches and the worry starts. If she doesn't come, will I sleep here all night? I don't have any money to call her. What will I do? In another childhood memory, I was lying in the back of our maroon van, curled up in a ball with tears hitting the worn and faded maroon carpet. I wanted her to protect me, hug me, and tell me everything is going to be okay. The story I believed was that my mom wasn't available to me, so I wouldn't bother her or ask her for help. She was too busy for me. She didn't have time to help. You need to figure everything out on your own, don't ask her. Don't be a bother.

I didn't ever want to be a problem for her. She was carrying so much already with the farm and all us kids. That she wasn't available was my truth, so I would keep my problems to myself. I didn't know how to tell her all the fear and worry I was carrying. I didn't know I could be vulnerable, not even around my mom. This hiding, coping alone, and not asking my mom to help me was an old story.

Back in the race, we met my mom and swapped out the water flasks. She cheered me on as I kept moving down the trail. My body eased a bit. *I can count on my mom. It's different now, I am different.*

The breeze felt great on my skin as I spotted Brindsley, Delaney, and Jeff on the trail ahead. They were at mile twelve with another hydration swap and a boost of energy as they cheered us along. My heart was full, seeing my children whooping it up for us. My son Brindsley came alongside me and started to run. The ache in my right hip quieted. I smiled as he looked up at me. "Mom, I'm going to run with you," he said. I was happy to have him along for a few minutes and forgot about the pace, the time, and the pain in my body. I let all the worries go. I appreciated this time. *He is growing up so fast, just like I heard the moment he was born.* It was true, and I wondered how I could make it slow down. My mind wandered into this realization then

I snapped out of it as I heard his voice again. "Mom, I'm turning around." Brindsley left me and I felt sad for a moment. I wanted him to run by me forever. *This is the hard part of motherhood. They will leave and go their way. I just hope there will be moments when they come back to run alongside me.*

The last twelve miles were a battle between my mind, body, and heart. I'd been here before, and maybe that's why I was so pissed at myself. I thought I was mentally tough, I thought I could handle this. I started yelling at myself and beating myself up. The old Julie was dominating, and I was the fearful child allowing it. *Oh, I hate that feeling! I hate when I can't find my courage and helpful thoughts.*

I allowed the pain to occupy my mind, and it became a major focus. I felt overwhelmed with the pain in my right hip, it was causing me to limp while tingling and burning were shooting down to my right knee into my calf muscle. My left foot throbbed with every push-off, and I felt my chest start to tighten. *Oh, Julie, you can't cry.* My thoughts came rushing in, *I don't know how to handle this pain, I'm limping so bad. Should I stop? I can't keep up with Felicia and Sam.* I couldn't stop the spiral. I couldn't focus. *I've dealt with pain similar to this at the Wineglass Marathon. Why can't I now?*

Maybe it was because there was no crowd to feed off of, no loud music or cheering. Maybe because there weren't other runners ahead of me, passing me or behind me. Or maybe I went into this virtual race with the pressure to perform perfectly with unrealistic expectations.

I was just coming off of a major setback five weeks prior and was unable to train for two weeks. I'm certain it was from the overindulgence of gluten and other things going on in my life. I'd woken up one morning and could hardly move. I knew I hadn't hurt myself sleeping but seriously? *I can't believe how debilitating my pain can be.* It just came out of nowhere. I had sores in my mouth and stomach pain. This was not new, so I reminded myself to stay calm. I went to my journal and answered these questions, and after I had a good cry.

What's going on in my life today? I'm home with children. I was furloughed from my job and thinking I need to look for a new job. I am uncertain about what to do because of COVID-19. Do I even go back to work? Do I change my career? I need to decide because a client has asked me to work with them. I'm not sure I can take him on with all the uncertainty. I don't want to let him down, but I don't think I can do this. What do I say? I don't know what to do. I'm training for the Virtual Boston Marathon. I'm supposed to run this morning.

What happened yesterday? I'm investigating homeschooling children and wondering if I should send them back to school. My thoughts are everywhere, and I feel a little panic making the decision. I don't know what to do. I don't want to be in so many roles. My friends are homeschooling their children. Jeff thinks it's best we send them back, that they will be fine wearing masks. I'm wondering if that will affect their mental health. We got into an argument. I got up early and ran. I didn't sleep well. My daughter was up several times. I ate gluten at lunch and dinner.

What's happening tomorrow? I need to make a few phone calls that I'm nervous about. I don't know what to say and anticipate a conflict. I don't know how to deal with conflicts. I have a run planned in the morning. The kids want to go swimming, and I planned on taking them to the community pool. I need to start packing up our things to move to our new home. I need to follow up about jobs.

Looking at my answers I could see the connections between what was happening in my life and what was happening in my body.

In the past, I would push through, beat myself up, and not ask for help. This time I made a few calls, one to my run coach, Joel, and one to my coach, Jen. They were both able to help me make sense of the pain, reflect, and provide me with the reassurance that this too shall pass. I got off the phone with a plan in place for how to handle the difficult phone calls I needed to make. I already felt some relief in my body. I'm so grateful to have both Joel and Jen in my corner.

Joel assured me that I had a great base going into the Virtual Marathon and to walk another week until I felt ready to run again. I just got back to my training two weeks before the Virtual Boston Marathon. My pace started slow, but I was able to get my cadence back to my approval for race day. I thought there wasn't a need to shift my expectations or performance. I didn't want to use this setback as an excuse, so I didn't recognize what I just went through five weeks ago. I was not giving myself any slack at all.

Felicia was ahead of me a bit and she dropped back to run next to me. I told her I was struggling and to go without me. I didn't want to hold her back. "You can do this Julie. I know you are in pain, but you can do this. I'm here with you," she said. I was so surprised that she wanted to stay with me and also very relieved. I needed someone to help me get to the finish. My family and friends were there waiting for me, and I didn't want to stop. I took a deep breath and searched my brain for the thoughts I know help me in these times. "I am a strong runner; I can do this." I changed my goal from a 3:25:00 finish to I'm going to finish this virtual race as best I can. I kept repeating, "I am a strong runner, I can do this."

The pain didn't stop, but I was determined to change my focus. I listened to the sounds of the birds, I brought my attention to the colorful red, orange, and yellow leaves, I glued my eyes on Sam's shirt as he glided ahead of me with ease and confidence. I focused on Felicia running beside me and fed off her pace and energy. I thought about how lucky I was to have a friend here with me.

With a mile and a half to go, a biker passed us and yelled out, "Awesome job, your family is waiting for you!" I managed to pick up the pace with that encouragement. As I got closer, I could hear the cheers from my family and friends. I could see my children holding up the finishing tape for me. I ran harder to get to them, my heart happy to see them. I crossed the finish, quickly stopped my watch, collapsing with my hands on my knees. I was so happy it was over. I was so tired. Jeff, Brindsley, Delaney, and mom came to hug me. I finished. I achieved my dream of racing the Boston Marathon! My dream finally came true. I never gave up and that makes me an endurance runner in sport and in life.

My family waiting for me

I always thought that racing marathons was a solitary sport, but I learned today that it's not. The crowd, the race officials, the volunteers, the other runners, they all matter. They pull you along, they push you from behind, and they give you the courage to keep going. Racing this virtual marathon showed me this. I'm so grateful for Felicia, Sam, my family, and friends that came to support me. I have a new appreciation for racing and feel this fullness in my heart.

The virtual Boston Marathon taught me that even in the solitude of running my experience without everyone mattered. Racing is better with everyone, just like life is. We aren't meant to do life alone.

This was exactly what I was doing for so many years, thinking I could do life alone. I was carrying all the guilt, shame, and pain around pretending it was fine. I didn't want to ask for help and thought the asking meant I was weak or stupid. I thought it meant I couldn't handle things and that was not a good character to have. I thought *I can't ask people for help; I need to figure it out*. I now believe I am strong to ask for help and the courage is in the asking.

Mom and Me

Felicia and Me: We did it!

The finish, "I'm so tired"

Conclusion

The Boston Marathon is not my foe
I've been training for years though
to run heartbreak hill
gonna be such a thrill
the pain couldn't stop me yo!

As I finish this book, I received the email that I've been anxiously waiting for.

Dear Julie Hughes - Congratulations! Your entry into the in-person 125th Boston Marathon on Monday, October 11, 2021, has been accepted.

We are going to Boston! No virtual race this time. I will finally run the course, hear the cheers, see the crowds, conquer Heartbreak Hill, and race with my fellow marathoners. This road to the Boston Marathon took longer than expected… 18 years to be exact, yet it was exactly how it was supposed to happen. This journey of suffering, heartache, and pain brought me to my truth, and it set me free. I love you, Julie. I made it. God is forever faithful. *Philippians 4:13, I can do all things through Christ who strengthens me.*

Me and my road: Third time's a charm

Epilogue

I have been 100% gluten-free since August 2020 and I haven't had a major setback or mouth sores since! Maybe I was diagnosed incorrectly, that this pain had nothing to do with psoriatic arthritis but with the food I was eating, my thoughts, and beliefs. I wanted to end this battle in my mind of "Do I, or don't I?" It has been a huge danger (DIMs) for me. This diagnosis has been taking up space in my brain that I could be using on something else. I want confirmation. I don't want to schedule appointments with a specialist that I may not need.

I went to another rheumatologist for my third opinion on April 6, 2021. I share the date with you to see that working through pain may take some time. However, I hope from my story you see that this is time not wasted. This was the time I needed to learn, heal, grow, and change. I'm grateful I was given the time to do this work. Patience, persistence, and courage were necessary, and my faith carried me when I started to question and doubt myself.

The third rheumatologist patiently listened to my entire story. I did my best to condense it where I could. She examined me, looked at past notes from other providers, and my blood work, and declared "You do not have fibromyalgia and you do not have psoriatic arthritis. You have psoriasis and by what you are telling me a gluten sensitivity. I would like you to continue with good nutrition, no gluten, and I will see you in a year. We will decide from there if I'm going to be of help to you." I could breathe, my shoulders relaxed, and a smile came to my face which was a huge brain triumph! I didn't give up. I was listening and trusting what my body was telling me. *WOOHOO!!!* I got home and opened my Protectometer handbook. I pulled the blue sticky notes "Things you hear" off the danger (DIMs) side. They read psoriatic arthritis and fibromyalgia. I ripped them up and threw them in the trash! *I DO NOT have psoriatic arthritis or fibromyalgia. I'm getting better at listening to the whispers of courage.*

I think back to all the peanut butter and jelly sandwiches I ate in my childhood. It was a part of my daily diet. I'm not sure this was a good habit especially now knowing I have a gluten sensitivity. Was gluten the issue then or did it come on later in life? I will never know. It doesn't matter. I know now that it's a factor, and I'm so glad I do! I have control over what I eat and put into my body. This is empowering. I'm listening to what foods feel good and letting go of the diets and styles of "how" to eat. Again, my mantra is, *Be the expert of me.* For some, gluten isn't a problem, which is great! For others, it's a huge problem. The best lesson I've learned on my road is to not be afraid to experiment, explore, and try again. Stay curious and keep going.

A Note to the Reader:

Pain real
No matter what
I see you; I hear you
I'm here to be with you always
Let's go

Pain is always real, no matter what is causing it. I'll write it
again. Pain is always real, no matter what is causing it. Pain
is always real, though it's tricky. Sometimes we feel pain in
a body part that is not the problem, such as my stomach
pain, weird nerve sensations in my feet, legs, and left big
toe. Nothing is wrong inside my stomach, but when I'm
stressed, worried, or afraid, that's how my body tells me,
that's where I can feel these emotions.

When I feel tingling and numbness in my feet outside of
my legs, I know that the nerves are not damaged. They are
talking to me and letting me know to change positions,
move, breath and be still, check in with my thoughts or
change my environment. My left big toe isn't injured, as I
once thought. The redness, pain, and swelling were the
result of eating gluten. That was how it showed up for me.

This mountain was a climb, and I can't explain how I kept
going other than my faith. God was helping me along even
though at times I didn't think I needed him. His grace
shined in places that I didn't expect. God gave me Jeff. Jeff
showed me love and that I'm worth loving. God gave me

my children. Becoming a mother gave me the courage to keep going, not to give up on myself, and showed me how to love and be loved. God gave me the gift of running, the love of running, and my dream of the Boston Marathon. My family was the light I needed to run out of the darkness.

I encourage you to rethink your pain, go after your dream and never give up. I'm here cheering you on every step of the way. If I can do it, so can you.

Action Plan

Pain is multi-dimensional. This is why placing me in a box of dos and don'ts based on my symptoms alone did not work. I have many options to improve my discomfort during a setback. Pain recovery is possible, and I proved that to myself. There was no magic in my recovery, no quick fix. It required me to face myself and challenge my thoughts and beliefs. Yet I also had to be willing to fail and try again. I've accepted that I will have pain in this life. I'm learning to come from a place of curiosity, compassion, and kindness instead of self-hatred and judgment.

What follows is my action plan, some of what I do during a setback. I found that when I hurt, I don't think straight, and I forget everything I've learned about pain! How inconvenient my brain can be. Having this written down in my journal has been helpful for me to remind myself that I've got this. This too shall pass, and I know what to do. I don't need to freak out.

1. Breathe: Place my hand on my heart, close my eyes, and take ten deep breaths in through the nose, out through the mouth and say, "I am loved, this is temporary."

2. Sleep hygiene: Set bedtime and wake-up time for the same time each day, darken and cool my bedroom, turn off screens one hour before bedtime, keep my journal and pen on the nightstand for when my mind

is busy, and I have trouble falling asleep. My brain can relax knowing my ideas are written down to easily access tomorrow.

3. Movement: Run, walk, yoga, strength train, and/or neurodynamics: The best movement is the one I like and feel good doing at that moment, and this may change.

4. Protectometer Handbook: What is out of balance today? Is there a danger I need to confront? Write down my safety in each category then take action.

5. Mindfulness or guided meditation: Use the insight timer app.

6. Curable app: Brain retraining, writing, meditation, pain neuroscience education.

7. Writing: Write out my thoughts, the sentences in my head, and then go through a model (Is it a thought that's actually contributing?). How I think about my pain matters. What am I making this pain mean?

8. Diet: Eat more Omega-3s, remain gluten-free & dairy-free, no processed food, no refined sugar, no corn, no soy, eat what feels good in my body.

9. Stress management: Get outdoors, make a gratitude list, read positive affirmations, watch a funny movie or

TV show with Jeff, play with Brindsley and Delaney, find ways to laugh.

10.   Word swap: Swap the word "pain" with "discomfort," swap "my back is stiff" with "my back is not as loose as I would like it."

11.   Connection: Spend time with Jeff, call a friend, meet up with a supportive friend, reach out to people in my corner (MD, coach, therapist) for help.

12.   Rest: find comfortable positions, be still, pray, and focus on my breath.

Acknowledgements

I want to thank:

My amazing, caring, patient, and supportive husband Jeff. Thank you for loving me no matter what and giving me the space to chase my dreams. I'm so grateful I get to do life with you.

My beautiful children Brindsley & Delaney: You are my miracles. You shined a light on my heart and soul just when I needed it most. Without you, this book wouldn't have been possible. I cherish the time I have with you both and I hope this book inspires you to never give up on your dreams. I love you to pieces and God loves you!

My brother Jon and sisters Mandy, Michelle, & Becky. I love you.

My sister-in-law Kristen, thank you for your feedback and support.

My sister-in-law Cindy, thank you for inspiring me to get back to running as a new mom (though you may not have known it at the time).

My mom and dad, thank you for teaching me grit, discipline, and strength to run. I love to run, and I like to think I'm good at it because of you. I love you. The dairy farm, it was a love-hate relationship yet a marathoner I became. I cherish the happy memories and what I've learned to become the person I am today.

Heartfelt thank you to my uncle and aunt, Tim and Colleen: Thank you for introducing me to the sport of running, taking me along on hiking adventures, and for your kindness. I love you both and am grateful to have you in my life.

My running buddy, Felicia thank you for meeting up in the dark, the freezing cold temperatures, and listening to my story. I treasure our morning runs each Saturday. It's friends like you that keep me going in this life.

My coaches, Joel Sattgast and Jen Liddy, thank you for believing in me. Your guidance, optimism, and tools got me to the other side. Thank you for providing me with a way forward and being in my corner. I'm so grateful we crossed paths.

My brilliant therapists Dr. Resnick and Dr. Taylor. Thank you for providing me a safe place to share what I needed, to move forward on my healing journey. You held space for me and listened. You guided me to heal my brain and face my pain challenge. I owe my life to you.

To Judy Gitenstein, with her decades in the industry, offered feedback on my draft. And to Laura Santo. Thank you for your patience and kindness. I appreciate the time and thoughtfulness you took.

A sincere thank you to Heather Peavey Johns, for copyediting this manuscript. Heather, I'm so grateful for your generosity and support. As a child, I would see you reading those enormous chapter books and it planted a seed for me. Thank you for being you. You are amazing.

To writing in community, you provided me a way to show up and keep writing even when self-doubt was consuming me. Thank you for your generous feedback, support, and for showing me the way. This book wouldn't have been possible without this community to lean on.

My morning writing group, Terri, Kathy, Wendy, Mic, Kartika, and Kymberly. A huge thank you for your encouragement, support, and cheering me on to the finish.

My Beta Readers: Marybeth, Jenny, Angela, & Felicia. Thank you for slogging with me especially with the first draft. I know it was full of mistakes and run-on sentences. Thank you for the feedback I greatly needed. Your time and support mean the world to me.

My laughter, Carrie-Anne, thank you for looking at about thirty book cover designs and not throwing your phone across the room! I'm so grateful for our friendship and the years in college we ran together. I love you.

Stacey, thank you for your endless friendship and support. You've been cheering me on since elementary school and

I'm so grateful for you. Thank you for not giving up on me.
I love you.

Kharyn, God brought us back together and I'm so grateful
to have you in my life. Thank you for your continued
prayers, support, and friendship. This life will give us
trouble but God, he put friends like you on my road to
press on. I love you.

My friends, in no particular order, who have supported me
along the way. Thank you and I love you. Bethany, Keri,
Abby, Liz, Tara, Jeanne, Leigh, Denise, Andrea, Cassi,
Anny, Cindy, Linda, Melissa, and Toni. Thank you for your
friendship and kindness. I'm so grateful to have you all in
my life and on my road.

My patients who over the years gave me the opportunity to
question and challenge my beliefs. Thank you for your
patience. My clients who entrusted me with their stories
and allowed me to walk alongside them on their pain
recovery journey. Thank you. You are brave, amazing, and
resilient.

My high school coaches, Jim Paccia and Michelle Rauber.
Coach Paccia I will never forget all the fun games you
added to our training and your constant encouragement.
You made running such a joy for me. Thank you. Coach
Rauber, thank you for always believing in me and
listening.

I will always remember the long run you ran with me when I was training for my first marathon. Thank you.

There are many people who have helped me along the way in my healing journey and creating this book. Thank you. Their generosity, smiles, encouragement, kindness allowed me to keep taking one turtle step forward. They checked in on my progress and told me they were proud of me.

Dr. Brene Brown, thank you for your research, your books, and the important work you do. Your books were a tool I needed for my healing and shined the light on shame. Thank you, I finally have the courage to name it.

Finally, to God. Thank you, Lord, for never leaving me even when I turned my back on you. Thank you for always loving me and for your endless grace and faithfulness. I love you, Lord. I pray this book gives you the glory.

About the Author

Julie Hughes is a licensed physical therapist and marathoner. She is proud to call herself a Boston Marathon finisher. She is grateful for the miles her body continues to let her run and hopes to join the ultramarathon scene. Julie lives in Manlius, NY with her husband and children. She would love to connect with you at the link below.

Run to Write Blog: Juliebhughes.substack.com

Made in the USA
Middletown, DE
07 December 2021

54500915R00151